Peter Sherran

REVISION PLUS

Edexcel
GCSE Mathematics
Foundation

Workbook

Contents

123	Number	Maths B – Units
4	Rounding Numbers	1, 2
5	Decimals	1, 2, 3
8	Number Properties	2
10	Whole Number Calculations	1, 2, 3
11	Integers	2, 3
13	Powers and Roots	2, 3
15	Order of Operations	1, 2, 3
16	Fractions	1, 2, 3
20	Percentages	1, 2, 3
23	Fractions, Decimals and Percentages	1, 2, 3
25	Everyday Maths	1, 3
27	Ratio and Proportion	1, 2
29	Estimating and Checking	1, 2

xy	Algebra	Maths B – Units
30	Algebraic Expressions	1, 2, 3
31	The Rules of Indices	2, 3
32	Substitution	2, 3
33	Brackets and Factorisation	2, 3
34	Linear Equations	3
36	Formulae	2, 3
38	Trial & Improvement	3
39	Sequences	2
41	Plotting Points	1, 2
42	Straight Line Graphs	1, 2
46	Linear Inequalities	3
47	Graphs of Quadratic Functions	3
49	Real-life Graphs	1, 2, 3

Contents

	Geometry	Maths B – Units
52	Angles	1, 2
54	Triangles	2, 3
56	Quadrilaterals	2, 3
57	Irregular Polygons	3
58	Regular Polygons	3
59	Symmetry	2
61	Congruence and Tessellation	2, 3
62	Similarity	2, 3
63	Pythagoras' Theorem	3
65	Perimeter	2
66	Area	2
68	Circles	2
70	Circles and Compound Area	3
71	Transformations	3
77	Constructions	3
80	Loci	3
81	3-D Shapes	2, 3
82	Nets and Elevations	2, 3
83	Volume	2, 3

	Measures	Maths B – Units
85	Maps and Scale Drawings	3
86	Enlargement, Perimeter, Area & Volume	3
87	Converting Measurements	1, 2
88	Bearings	3
89	Compound Measures	2
90	Measuring Lines and Angles	1, 2

	Probability	Maths B – Units
91	Probability	1

	Statistics	Maths B – Units
95	Problem Solving and Data Handling	1
96	Collecting Data	1
98	Sorting Data	1
101	Displaying Data	1
106	Averages and Spread	1
108	Unstructured Exam-style Questions	
112	Notes	

Rounding Numbers

1 Round...

a) 7.321 to... **i)** 1 decimal place .... **ii)** 2 decimal places ....

b) 16.781 to... **i)** 1 decimal place .... **ii)** 2 decimal places ....

c) 0.01765 to...**i)** 2 decimal places .... **ii)** 3 decimal places ....

d) 0.1053 to... **i)** 1 decimal place .... **ii)** 3 decimal places ....

e) 7.0707 to... **i)** 1 decimal place .... **ii)** 2 decimal places ....

2 Dave's weight is measured in kg to 2 decimal places. This value rounds to 68.4kg to 1 decimal place. What is the lowest measurement and the highest measurement possible for his actual weight to 2 decimal places?

Lowest possible weight: .... Highest possible weight: ....

3 Helen's height is measured in metres to 3 decimal places. This value rounds to 1.65m to 2 decimal places. What is the lowest measurement and the highest measurement possible for her actual height to 3 decimal places?

Lowest possible height: .... Highest possible height: ....

4 Round...

a) 432 to... **i)** 1 significant figure .... **ii)** 2 significant figures ....

b) 9154 to... **i)** 1 significant figure .... **ii)** 2 significant figures ....

c) 10 047 to... **i)** 2 significant figures...................................... **ii)** 4 significant figures ....

d) 0.0238 to... **i)** 1 significant figure .... **ii)** 2 significant figures ....

e) 0.000 1736 to... **i)** 2 significant figures.............................. **ii)** 3 significant figures ....

f) 0.010 366 to... **i)** 2 significant figures............................... **ii)** 3 significant figures ....

5 The attendance at a pop concert was 5700 to 2 significant figures. What is the difference between the lowest possible actual attendance and the highest possible actual attendance?

....

....

---

6 Round 135.6742 to **a)** 1 decimal place **b)** 2 decimal places **c)** 1 significant figure
d) 2 significant figures **e)** 3 significant figures

7 Round 0.060 38 to **a)** 1 decimal place **b)** 2 decimal places **c)** 3 decimal places
d) 1 significant figure **e)** 2 significant figures **f)** 3 significant figures

8 Fran's weight is measured in kg to 2 decimal places. The value is rounded to 47.6kg to 1 decimal place. What is the difference between her highest possible weight and her lowest possible weight to 2 decimal places?

9 **a)** Use your calculator to work out the value of $(1.46)^2 \times 6.71$. Write down all the digits on your display.
b) Round your answer to a suitable degree of accuracy.

1 Complete the following table (the first row has been done for you).

Place Value of Digits							Decimal Number
100 Hundreds	10 Tens	1 Units	DECIMAL POINT •	$\frac{1}{10}$ Tenths	$\frac{1}{100}$ Hundredths	$\frac{1}{1000}$ Thousandths	
		3		4	2		3.42
a) 1	0	2		5			....
b)	1	3		4	7	1	....
c)		....		....	....	....	8.407
d)	9	0		0	3	1	....
e)	....	....		....	....	....	423.008

2 Use a calculator to write each of the following four decimal places.

a) $\frac{2}{3}$ .... b) $\frac{2}{5}$ .... c) $\frac{1}{11}$ .... d) $\frac{7}{9}$ ....

3 Arrange the following decimals in ascending (lowest to highest) order of value:

6.3   0.36   3.6   0.306   0.63

....

4 Write the following fractions as decimals, to four decimal places.

a) $\frac{3}{8}$ b) $\frac{2}{9}$ c) $\frac{1}{30}$ d) $\frac{22}{25}$ e) $\frac{4}{15}$

5 Arrange the following decimals in descending (highest to lowest) order:

14.32   1.432   143.2   13.42   14.23   1.342

6 Complete the following additions and subtractions without using a calculator. Show all your working.

a) 13.62 + 7.77   b) 103.2 + 4.837   c) 40.75 – 8.29   d) 723.4 – 6.19

7 Mrs Green goes shopping. She buys four tins of baked beans at 37p each, three tins of spaghetti at 29p each and two boxes of cornflakes at £1.37 each. She pays for her goods with a £10 note. How much change does she receive?

8 Peter puts three boxes in the boot of his car. They weigh 8.4kg, 6.73kg and 13.03kg. What is the total weight of the load?

Decimals

1 Solve the following without using a calculator. Where possible show all your working.

a) 4.7 × 10   b) 13.246 × 10   c) 0.00146 × 100   d) 136.3 × 1000

....

e) 7.56 × 13   f) 4.72 × 2.3

....

g) 16.56 × 17.3   h) 4.713 × 1.56

....

2 If 27 × 36 = 972 write down, without making any further calculations, the value of...

a) 2.7 × 36 ....   b) 27 × 0.36 ....   c) 2.7 × 3.6 ....

d) 0.027 × 36 ....   e) 0.27 × 0.36 ....

3 If 231 × 847 = 195 657 write down, without making any further calculations, the value of...

a) 0.231 × 847 ....   b) 231 × 84 700 ....

c) 0.231 × 847 000 ....   d) 2310 × 8.47 ....

4 Solve the following without using a calculator.
Where possible show all your working.
 a) 15.67 × 10   b) 0.0101 × 100   c) 3.4671 × 1000   d) 2.32 × 11
 e) 4.67 × 1.8   f) 146.2 × 2.45   g) 13.33 × 0.23   h) 9.4 × 0.003

5 If 3.52 × 4.7 = 16.544 write down, without making any further
 calculations, the value of...
 a) 352 × 47   b) 3.52 × 47   c) 0.352 × 4.7   d) 3.52 × 0.047

6 A school holds a raffle. The three prizes cost £24.65,
 £17.99 and £9.89. 130 tickets were sold at £1.25 each.
 How much profit did the school make from the raffle?

7 Jim is going to hire a cement mixer. The cost is £24.50 for the first
 day and £3.75 for each extra day. Jim wants to hire it for 7 days.
 How much will it cost him in total?

8 A shirt costs £24.95. How much is this in euros if £1 = €1.60?

£24.95

Decimals

1 Solve the following without using a calculator. Where possible show all your working.

a) 16.3 ÷ 10   **b)** 0.347 ÷ 10   **c)** 14 632.4 ÷ 100   **d)** 1.2467 ÷ 1000

....

e) 37.6 ÷ 8   **f)** 41.04 ÷ 1.2

....

....

g) 1141.72 ÷ 0.23   **h)** 549.6 ÷ 1.2

....

....

2 If 72.8 ÷ 56 = 1.3 write down, without making any further calculations, the value of...

a) 72.8 ÷ 5.6 ....   **b)** 7.28 ÷ 56 ....   **c)** 72.8 ÷ 0.56 ....

d) 0.728 ÷ 56 ....   **e)** 728 ÷ 56 ....

3 If 27 × 34 = 918 write down, without making any further calculations, the value of...

a) 918 ÷ 27 ....   **b)** 918 ÷ 3.4 ....   **c)** 91.8 ÷ 27 ....

d) 9.18 ÷ 3.4 ....   **e)** 91.8 ÷ 340 ....

---

4 Solve the following without using a calculator. Where possible show all your working.
   a) 7.162 ÷ 10   **b)** 0.0034 ÷ 100   **c)** 473.1 ÷ 1000   **d)** 707.4 ÷ 9   **e)** 24.64 ÷ 1.4   **f)** 0.087 88 ÷ 0.0013

5 If 58.82 ÷ 3.4 = 17.3 write down, without making any further calculations, the value of...
   a) 58.82 ÷ 0.34   **b)** 5882 ÷ 0.34   **c)** 58.82 ÷ 17.3   **d)** 3.4 × 17.3

6 A school holds a raffle. The three prizes cost £9.49, £14.99 and £19.99. Tickets cost 75p each.
   What is the minimum number of tickets that need to be sold for the school to make a profit?

7 Jean is going to hire a wallpaper stripper. The cost is £8.50 for the first day and £1.25 for each extra day.
   When she returns the wallpaper stripper the total hire charge is £24.75. For how many days did she hire the
   wallpaper stripper?

Number Properties

1 **Here are eight numbers:**

$$3 \quad 4 \quad 6 \quad 7 \quad 11 \quad 15 \quad 20 \quad 21$$

a) Which three numbers are even numbers? ....

b) Which two numbers are factors of 40? ....

c) Which two numbers are factors of 45? ....

d) Which four numbers are factors of 42? ....

e) Which two numbers are multiples of 7? ....

f) Which three numbers are multiples of 2? ....

g) Which three numbers are prime numbers? ....

h) Which number has an odd number of factors? ....

2 **Here are ten numbers:**

$$5 \quad 8 \quad 11 \quad 19 \quad 22 \quad 24 \quad 31 \quad 36 \quad 47 \quad 81$$

a) Which six numbers are odd numbers? ....

b) Which three numbers are factors of 72? ....

c) Which three numbers are factors of 110? ....

d) Which three numbers are multiples of 3? ....

e) Which three numbers are multiples of 4? ....

f) Which five numbers are prime numbers? ....

g) Which two numbers have an odd number of factors? ....

3 **What is the reciprocal of...**

a) 8? ....   b) 25? ....   c) 0.5? ....   d) $\frac{3}{4}$? ....

4 **The reciprocal of a number is 0.1**

What is the number? ....

5 **Express the following numbers in prime factor form:**

a) 36   b) 64   c) 930

....

6 What are **a)** the highest common factor and **b)** the lowest common multiple of:

i) 20 and 36

   a) ....

   b) ....

ii) 60 and 100

   a) ....

   b) ....

iii) 15 and 18

   a) ....

   b) ....

iv) 40 and 58?

   a) ....

   b) ....

7 What is the highest common factor and the lowest common multiple of ...

a) 6, 15 and 24?

....

b) 15, 18 and 24

....

8 **a)** The highest common factor of two numbers is 4. The lowest common multiple of the same two numbers is 60. What are the two numbers?

....

....

b) The highest common factor of three numbers is 15. The lowest common multiple of the same three numbers is 90. What are the three numbers?

....

....

9 **Here are ten numbers:**

   9   14   25   29   41   50   61   70   84   100

   a) Which three numbers are **i)** factors of 200, **ii)** multiples of 25, **iii)** multiples of 7, **iv)** prime numbers?

   b) Which of the above numbers has the reciprocal 0.02?

10 **What is the reciprocal of a)** 100, **b)** $\frac{1}{100}$, **c)** 0.01, **d)** $\frac{99}{100}$?

11 **Express the following numbers in prime factor form: a)** 30, **b)** 100, **c)** 2048

12 **What is the highest common factor and lowest common multiple of...**

   a) 15 and 18, **b)** 40 and 58, **c)** 15, 18 and 24?

Whole Number Calculations

1 **Solve the following without using a calculator. Show all your working.**

a)
```
   475
 +  28
```

b)
```
  23179
 + 4830
```

c)
```
   238
 −  99
```

d)
```
  43008
 − 1559
```

e)
```
   423
 ×  36
```

f)
```
  4705
 ×   91
```

g)

16 ⟌ 608

h)

13 ⟌ 3341

i) 41 × 100

j) 573 × 1000

k) 423 ÷ 10

l) 8 ÷ 1000

2 **a)** A whole number is multiplied by 1000 giving an answer of 234 000

What is the number? ....

b) A whole number is divided by 100 giving an answer of 0.08

What is the number? ....

3 **a)** The number 864 900 is divided by a power of 10 to give the answer 8.649

What is the power of 10 used?

....

b) The number 763 is multiplied by a power of 10 to give the answer 76 300 000

What is the power of 10 used?

....

4 **Solve the following without using a calculator. Show all your working.**
a) 3001 + 999   b) 4735 + 381 + 49   c) 4079 − 497   d) 13 574 − 9281   e) 473 × 67   f) 375 × 413
g) 4037 ÷ 11   h) 47 748 ÷ 23   i) 940 × 10   j) 403 × 100   k) 11 × 1000   l) 33 942 × 10 000
m) 408 ÷ 10   n) 55 ÷ 100   o) 6 ÷ 100   p) 33 942 ÷ 10 000

5 **A whole number is multiplied by a power of 10 giving an answer of 23 000. When the whole number is divided by the same power of 10 the answer is 2.3 a)** What is the whole number?
b) What is the power of 10?

1 **a)** Put the following integers into ascending order (lowest to highest):

14   -3   -1   5   12   -7   -11   2

....

b) Put the following integers into descending order (highest to lowest):

-230   467   165   -62   -162   70   -320   8

....

2 **Complete the following boxes:**

a) i) $1 - 3 + \boxed{} = 6$ **ii)** $6 + \boxed{} = 2$ **iii)** $-6 + \boxed{} = -11$

iv) $-4 - \boxed{} = -9$ **v)** $4 - \boxed{} = -4$ **vi)** $-3 - \boxed{} = 5$

vii) $-6 \times \boxed{} = 12$ **viii)** $5 \times \boxed{} = -20$ **ix)** $-6 \times \boxed{} = 6$

x) $-12 \div \boxed{} = -2$ **xi)** $36 \div \boxed{} = -9$ **xii)** $-45 \div \boxed{} = 9$

b) i) $-4 - 6 + \boxed{} = 2$ **ii)** $6 - \boxed{} - 3 = 11$ **iii)** $-8 - 3 - \boxed{} = 5$

iv) $\boxed{} + 2 - 5 = -9$ **v)** $14 - 1 + \boxed{} = -15$ **vi)** $4 - 11 + \boxed{} = -5$

c) i) $\dfrac{-6 + \boxed{}}{-3} = 7$ **ii)** $\dfrac{-6 + 2 - \boxed{}}{-5} = 4$ **iii)** $\dfrac{\boxed{} - 6 - 3}{-1} = 4$

iv) $\dfrac{-3 \times -5 \times \boxed{}}{-6} = 10$ **v)** $\dfrac{9 \times \boxed{} \times -2}{4 - 6} = 9$

d) i) $\boxed{} + \boxed{} = -4$ **ii)** $\boxed{} - \boxed{} = -3$ **iii)** $\boxed{} \times \boxed{} = -18$

iv) $\boxed{} \div \boxed{} = -10$ **v)** $\boxed{} \times -5 \times \boxed{} = 30$

3 **Complete the following calculations by inserting =, +, −, × or ÷ into the correct boxes:**

a) $6 \boxed{} 9 \boxed{} -3$ **b)** $2 \boxed{} 3 \boxed{} -7 \boxed{} 12$

c) $9 \boxed{} 1 \boxed{} -3 \boxed{} -3$ **d)** $-50 \boxed{} 10 \boxed{} 5 \boxed{} 0$

e) $6 \boxed{} -3 \boxed{} 10 \boxed{} 19 \boxed{} 1$

f) $10 \boxed{} -2 \boxed{} 6 \boxed{} 2 \boxed{} 0$

Integers

4 The following table shows the highest temperatures (in °C) for eight places on a particular day:

Place	Athens	Berlin	Cairo	Cardiff	London	Madrid	Moscow	New York
Temperature	15	-2	25	2	6	13	-6	18

a) What is the difference in temperature between the following places:

i) Athens and Berlin? ....

ii) Cairo and Moscow? ....

iii) Berlin and Moscow? ....

b) The following day the temperature in Cardiff had fallen by 2°C and the temperature in Moscow had fallen by 5°C. What was the new difference in temperature between Cardiff and Moscow?

....

5 Below is part of a bank statement:

LONSDALE BUILDING SOCIETY

Date	Description	Deposit	Withdrawal	Balance
11/12/03				£226.30
12/12/03	The Toy Shop		-£49.99	£176.31
13/12/03	Gas Bill		-£21.03	£155.28
13/12/03	Cheque	£25.00		£180.28
16/12/03	La Trattoria		-£32.98	[ ]
19/12/03	Rent		[ ]	-£112.70

a) What was the balance on 16/12/03 after the withdrawal of £32.98?

....

b) On 19/12/03 there was a withdrawal to pay for rent. How much was the withdrawal?

....

6 Put the following integers into ascending order:

3   -3   -11   0   4   19   -36   74   -1   100

7 Complete the following:

a) $6 - 8 =$ b) $-4 - 4 =$ c) $-1 - 1 + 2 =$ d) $-5 \times -6 \times 10 =$ e) $-5 \times 3 \times 6 =$ f) $-15 \div 3 \times -4 =$ g) $100 \div 4 \times -1 =$

8 Complete the following boxes:

a) $\boxed{} - 3 = 12$ b) $-8 - \boxed{} = 3$ c) $-6 + \boxed{} - 2 = 11$ d) $-14 + 20 + \boxed{} = -10$ e) $\boxed{} + 4 - 8 = -15$

Powers and Roots

1 **Work out the value of...**

a) 2^3 .... b) 3^2 .... c) 4^3 ....

d) 10^3 .... e) 5^3 .... f) 6^2 ....

2 **Here are ten numbers:**

10   18   25   27   45   64   80   125   133   196

a) Which three numbers are square numbers? ....

b) Which three numbers are cube numbers? ....

c) Which one of these numbers is a square number and a cube number? ....

d) Which of the above numbers is equal to 4^3? ....

e) Which of the above numbers is equal to $10^2 - 6^2$? ....

f) Which of the above numbers is equal to $4^3 + 2^4$? ....

3 **Work out the value of...**

a) $\sqrt{25}$ .... b) $\sqrt{9}$ .... c) $\sqrt{144}$ ....

d) $\sqrt{121}$ .... e) $\sqrt{49}$ .... f) 1^3 ....

g) $\sqrt[3]{8}$ .... h) $\sqrt[3]{216}$ .... i) 7^3 ....

4 **Here are ten numbers:**

2   4   5   8   10   20   27   36   64   80

a) Which three numbers have an integer square root? ....

b) Which three numbers have an integer cube root? ....

c) Which one of these numbers has an integer square root and an integer cube root? ....

d) Which of the above numbers is equal to $\sqrt{144} - \sqrt[3]{8}$? ....

e) Which of the above numbers is equal to $\sqrt{81} \times \sqrt{16}$? ....

5 **Work out the value of...**

a) 10^2 .... b) 10^3 .... c) 10^4 ....

d) 10^5 .... e) 10^6 .... f) 10^7 ....

6 **What is 100 000 000 as a power of ten?**

....

Powers and Roots

7 Work out the value of...

a) $(-3)^2$ ....

b) $(-3)^3$ ....

c) $(-5)^2$ ....

d) $(-5)^3$ ....

e) $(-1)^2$ ....

f) $(-1)^3$ ....

8 Find the value of...

a) $2^3 \times 2^2$ ....

b) $3^2 \times 3^1$ ....

c) $4^3 \times 4^2 \times 4^1$ ....

d) $2^3 \div 2^2$ ....

e) $10^4 \div 10^2$ ....

f) $6^4 \div 6^0$ ....

g) $\dfrac{10^2 - 6^2}{4^3}$ ....

h) $\dfrac{4^3 + 2^6}{8^2}$ ....

9 a) What is $3^2 \times 9$ as a single power of 3? ....

b) What is $4^2 \times 2^3$ as a single power of 2? ....

c) What is $8^2 \times 2^4$ as a single power of 4? ....

10 Work out the value of...

a) $25^{\frac{1}{2}}$ ....

b) $36^{\frac{1}{2}}$ ....

c) $144^{\frac{1}{2}}$ ....

d) $196^{\frac{1}{2}}$ ....

e) $64^{\frac{1}{3}}$ ....

f) $\sqrt[3]{1}$ ....

g) $8^{\frac{1}{3}}$ ....

h) $\sqrt[3]{1000}$ ....

i) $27^{\frac{1}{3}}$ ....

11 a) What is $\sqrt{4} \times 8$ as a single power of 4? ....

b) What is $\sqrt[3]{27} \times 3$ as a single power of 3? ....

c) What is $\sqrt[3]{64} \times 16^{\frac{1}{2}}$ as a single power of 2? ....

---

12 Work out the value of...

a) 4^3 b) 4^1 c) $4^3 \times 4^1$ d) $4^3 \times 5^2$ e) $8^2 + 3^3$

f) $10^2 + 3^3 + 5$ g) $6^2 - 3^2$ h) $\dfrac{8^2}{2^2}$ i) $\dfrac{3^3 - 7}{2^2}$

13 What is $3^3 \times 9^2$ as a single power of 3?

14 Work out the value of...

a) $169^{\frac{1}{2}}$ b) $\sqrt[3]{125}$ c) $\sqrt{81}$ d) $125^{\frac{1}{3}}$ e) $225^{\frac{1}{2}}$

15 Find the value of...

a) $(\sqrt{9})^3$ b) $(\sqrt[3]{8})^2$

Order of Operations

1 **Calculate the following:**

a) $7 + 5 \times 2$

....

....

b) $14 \times 5 - 3$

....

....

c) $6^2 + 4 \times 2$

....

....

d) $\dfrac{15}{3} + 6$

....

....

e) $18 \times 2 - 5^2$

....

....

f) $\dfrac{30}{6} - \dfrac{40}{10}$

....

....

g) $2^3 + 4^3 \times 3$

....

....

h) $6 \times 7 - 10 \times 3 + 8$

....

....

i) $15 - 3 \times 6 \times 2 + 5$

....

....

2 Put brackets in the following so that each calculation is correct:

a) $13 - 3 \times 4 + 3 = 43$

b) $13 - 3 \times 4 + 3 = -8$

c) $13 - 3 \times 4 + 3 = 70$

d) $13 - 3 \times 4 + 3 = 4$

e) $3 \times 1.4 + 4 \times 2.5 = 20.5$

f) $7 + 3.2 \times 6 - 4.4 = 12.12$

3 **Calculate the following:**
    a) $4 + 3 \times 13$ **b)** $4 \times 3 - 13$ **c)** $4 - 3 \times 13$ **d)** $4^2 \div 2 + 3$ **e)** $9 + 15 \div 5$ **f)** $4 + 7 \times 3 - 15$
    g) $14 \div 4 - 5$ **h)** $3 + 7 - 5 \times 3^2$

4 **Put brackets in the following expression so that its value is...**   **a)** -1   **b)** 35   **c)** -51
    $3^2 - 4 \times 5 + 10$

5 **Put brackets in the following expression so that its value is...**   **a)** 54   **b)** -2   **c)** 6
    $4^2 - 3 \times 4 + 2$

Fractions

1 Complete the following equivalent fractions.

a) $\dfrac{3}{4} = \dfrac{\square}{12}$

b) $\dfrac{5}{7} = \dfrac{\square}{28}$

c) $\dfrac{5}{9} = \dfrac{30}{\square}$

d) $\dfrac{4}{11} = \dfrac{16}{\square} = \dfrac{\square}{33}$

e) $\dfrac{9}{16} = \dfrac{90}{\square} = \dfrac{36}{\square}$

f) $\dfrac{21}{25} = \dfrac{\square}{100} = \dfrac{63}{\square}$

2 Complete the following equivalent fractions.

a) $\dfrac{15}{25} = \dfrac{\square}{5}$

b) $\dfrac{24}{36} = \dfrac{\square}{3}$

c) $\dfrac{9}{18} = \dfrac{1}{\square}$

d) $\dfrac{60}{80} = \dfrac{6}{\square} = \dfrac{\square}{4}$

e) $\dfrac{16}{32} = \dfrac{4}{\square} = \dfrac{1}{\square}$

f) $\dfrac{36}{42} = \dfrac{\square}{21} = \dfrac{6}{\square}$

3 Insert > or < to compare these fractions.

a) $\dfrac{4}{5} \;\square\; \dfrac{3}{5}$

b) $\dfrac{7}{9} \;\square\; \dfrac{5}{9}$

c) $\dfrac{12}{25} \;\square\; \dfrac{11}{25}$

d) $\dfrac{8}{11} \;\square\; \dfrac{15}{22}$

e) $\dfrac{7}{10} \;\square\; \dfrac{19}{30}$

f) $\dfrac{4}{9} \;\square\; \dfrac{23}{45}$

4 Here are eight fractions:

$$\dfrac{35}{50} \qquad \dfrac{16}{40} \qquad \dfrac{60}{90} \qquad \dfrac{28}{40} \qquad \dfrac{30}{40} \qquad \dfrac{40}{100} \qquad \dfrac{84}{120} \qquad \dfrac{10}{25}$$

a) Which three fractions are equivalent to $\dfrac{2}{5}$? ....

b) Which three fractions are equivalent to $\dfrac{7}{10}$? ....

5 Express the following fractions in their simplest form:

a) $\dfrac{27}{30}$ ....

b) $\dfrac{42}{6}$ ....

c) $\dfrac{84}{105}$ ....

d) $\dfrac{108}{184}$ ....

6 **a)** Arrange the following fractions in ascending (lowest to highest) order:

$\frac{5}{6}$ $\frac{3}{5}$ $\frac{11}{15}$ $\frac{2}{3}$ $\frac{1}{2}$

....

....

b) Arrange the following fractions in descending (highest to lowest) order:

$\frac{9}{40}$ $\frac{3}{5}$ $\frac{5}{8}$ $\frac{9}{10}$ $\frac{1}{4}$

....

....

7 **Write down two fractions that are greater than $\frac{7}{10}$ but less than $\frac{5}{6}$.**

....

....

8 **a)** Write the following improper fractions as mixed numbers:

i) $\frac{11}{5}$ ....   **ii)** $\frac{13}{6}$ ....   **iii)** $\frac{24}{5}$ ....   **iv)** $\frac{32}{3}$ ....

....

b) Write the following mixed numbers as improper fractions:

i) $3\frac{1}{3}$ ....   **ii)** $5\frac{1}{4}$ ....   **iii)** $11\frac{3}{5}$ ....   **iv)** $20\frac{1}{20}$ ....

....

9 **Write down three fractions that are equivalent to each of the following:**
a) $\frac{2}{3}$ **b)** $\frac{4}{7}$ **c)** $\frac{9}{11}$

10 **Express the following fractions in their simplest form and then arrange them into ascending order:**

$\frac{28}{35}$ $\frac{38}{40}$ $\frac{75}{100}$ $\frac{42}{84}$ $\frac{99}{110}$

11 **Write down three fractions that are greater than $\frac{4}{5}$ but less than $\frac{9}{10}$.**

Fractions

1. Solve the following calculations without using a calculator. Show all your working and give your answers in their simplest form.

a) $\frac{3}{4} + \frac{2}{3}$ ....

b) $\frac{2}{9} + \frac{7}{8}$ ....

c) $4\frac{1}{2} + 2\frac{9}{10}$ ....

d) $7\frac{5}{8} + 4\frac{1}{3}$ ....

e) $\frac{9}{10} - \frac{1}{2}$ ....

f) $\frac{13}{15} - \frac{2}{3}$ ....

g) $4\frac{4}{5} - 1\frac{3}{8}$ ....

h) $9\frac{1}{6} - 4\frac{3}{5}$ ....

2. At a football match the crowd is made up as follows:

$\frac{5}{12}$ of the crowd are over 40 years old, $\frac{1}{4}$ of the crowd is between 20 years old and 40 years old, and the remainder of the crowd is less than 20 years old.

What fraction of the crowd is less than 20 years old? Give your answer in its simplest form.

....

....

....

....

3. Solve the following calculations without using a calculator. Show all your working and give your answers in their simplest form.

a) $\frac{1}{4} \times \frac{2}{5}$ ....

b) $\frac{9}{10} \times \frac{2}{7}$ ....

c) $\frac{3}{4} \div \frac{9}{10}$ ....

d) $\frac{7}{8} \div \frac{7}{12}$ ....

e) $\frac{1}{2} \times \frac{3}{5}$ ....

f) $\frac{1}{4} \times \frac{5}{7}$ ....

g) $\frac{1}{2} \div \frac{2}{3}$ ....

h) $\frac{1}{2} \div \frac{1}{4}$ ....

i) $\frac{8}{9} \times 3$ ....

j) $\frac{7}{10} \div 3$ ....

4. Solve the following calculations without using a calculator. Show all your working.

a) $\frac{7}{10} + \frac{5}{8}$ b) $2\frac{1}{3} + 4\frac{3}{8}$ c) $\frac{9}{10} - \frac{2}{3}$ d) $4\frac{1}{2} - 3\frac{7}{10}$ e) $\frac{2}{5} \times \frac{7}{10}$ f) $\frac{13}{15} \div \frac{4}{5}$

g) $4\frac{1}{2} \times 5$ h) $2\frac{1}{3} \div 6$

Fractions

1 James wants to buy an mp3 player that costs £240. He pays $\frac{1}{8}$ of the cost as a deposit. How much deposit did James pay?

....

....

2 Mary buys a new car that costs £13 000. She pays $\frac{2}{5}$ of the cost as a deposit. She pays the remainder monthly over a period of four years.

a) How much deposit does Mary pay?

....

....

b) What is her monthly repayment?

....

....

c) At the end of the four years Mary decides to sell her car. It is now worth £7150. Express its value now, after four years, as a fraction of its value when new. Give your answer in the simplest form.

....

....

3 A shop holds a sale where all items are reduced by $\frac{1}{6}$.

a) Calculate the sale price of an item that cost £93.60 before the sale.

....

....

b) The sale price of another item is £121.50. Calculate its price before it was reduced.

....

....

4 A football match lasts $1\frac{1}{2}$ hours. During the match, player number 9 sits on the bench for a total of 15 minutes. He is on the pitch for the rest of the time. Express the total length of time that player number 9 is on the pitch as a fraction of the time that the match lasts. Give your answer in its simplest form.

5 In a sale, a washing machine has its original price reduced by $\frac{1}{2}$. The following week the sale price is further reduced by $\frac{1}{4}$.
a) If the washing machine originally cost £600, calculate its sale price after **i)** the first reduction, **ii)** the second reduction.
b) If a washing machine in the same sale costs £150 after both reductions what was its original price?

6 Express 40 seconds as a fraction of 1 hour.

Percentages

1 **Calculate the following amounts:**

a) 20% of 60p ....

....

b) 30% of 6.5km ....

....

2 **Express...**

a) £18 as a percentage of £90 ....

....

b) 42cm as a percentage of 8.4m ....

....

3 **Alan has kept a record of his height and weight from when he was age 10 and age 16.**

Age 10	1.2m tall	40kg weight
Age 16	1.74m tall	64kg weight

a) i) Calculate the increase in his height from age 10 to age 16 ....

ii) Express this increase as a percentage of his height at age 10

....

b) i) Calculate the increase in his weight from age 10 to age 16 ....

ii) Express this increase as a percentage of his weight at age 10

....

4 **A train ticket costs £17.60 when bought on the day of travel. If the same ticket is bought in advance it costs £15.40. Express the saving you make when you buy the ticket in advance as a percentage of the full ticket price when bought on the day of travel.**

....

....

5 **Calculate the following amounts:**
a) 45% of £2.60 **b)** 80% of 6.4kg **c)** 5% of £10.40.

6 **a)** Express 46cm as a percentage of 69cm **b)** Express 200m as a percentage of 200km
c) Express 550g as a percentage of 2kg.

7 **A tin of tomato soup weighs 420g. Special tins weigh 546g. Calculate how much heavier a special tin is compared to a normal tin as a percentage of the weight of a normal tin.**

8 **A brand new car bought in the UK costs £18 000. The same car bought abroad costs £14 850. Calculate the decrease in the price when the car is bought abroad as a percentage of its price in the UK.**

Percentages

1 A brand new car costs £15 000. It is estimated that it will decrease in value by 23% in the first year. What is the estimated value of the car at the end of the first year?

....

....

2 The average attendance at a football club over a season was 32 500. In the next season there was a 6% increase in the average attendance. What was the average attendance for that season?

....

....

3 Mr and Mrs Smith bought a house for £120 000. Each year since the value of the property has increased by 10%.

a) Calculate the value of the house 2 years after they bought it.

....

....

b) What would the value of the property be after 2 years if the rate of increase was 5% per year?

....

....

4 Jim buys a new motorbike for £10 000.

a) The value of the motorbike decreases by 20% in its first year after purchase. What is the value of the motorbike at the end of the year?

....

....

....

....

b) The motorbike decreases in value by a further 10% in its second year after purchase. What is its value after 2 years?

....

....

5 An electrical shop has a sale. All items are reduced by 20%. The following week the shop takes 10% off its sale prices. Pat wants to buy a fridge that was priced at £100 before the sale. She reckons that she will save 30% of this price and that the fridge will now cost her £70. Is she correct? Explain why.

6 A bottle of ink weighs 220g. Calculate the weight of a bottle which is $12\frac{1}{2}$% heavier.

Percentages

1. Phil has been told by his mum that he needs to spend 1 hour a day doing his homework, an increase of 50%. How long did Phil originally spend doing his homework each day?

....

....

2. An electrical shop has a sale. All items are reduced by 15%. A tumble dryer has a sale price of £122.40. What was the price of the tumble dryer before the sale?

....

....

3. A man buys an antique clock. He later sells it for £5040, an increase of 12% on the price he paid for it. How much did the clock cost him?

....

....

....

....

4. Dave is a long distance lorry driver. On Tuesday he drives 253km. This is a 15% increase on the distance he drove the previous day. How far did he drive on Monday?

....

....

5. Jean has her house valued. It is worth £84 000. This is a 40% increase on the price she originally paid for it. How much did Jean pay for her house?

....

....

6. A clothes shop has a sale. All prices are reduced by 30%. The sale price of a dress is £86.80. What was the original price of the dress?

....

....

7. Mrs Smith buys some shares. In twelve months their value has increased by 15% to £3680. How much did she pay for the shares?

....

....

8. Mr Jones collects stamps. After two years he has increased the number of stamps in his collection by 120% to 660. How many stamps did he have in his collection two years ago?

....

Fractions, Decimals and Percentages

1 Complete the following table. The first row has been done for you.

Fraction (simplest form)	Decimal	Percentage
$\frac{1}{2}$	0.5	50%
a) $\frac{3}{10}$	....	....
b)	0.45	....
c)	....	37.5%
d) $\frac{2}{3}$	....	....
e)	0.125	....
f)	....	84%
g) $1\frac{4}{5}$	....	....
h)	4.6	....
i)	....	225%

2 $\frac{3}{5}$ of the CDs in Peter's collection are pop music. Is this more or less than 55% of his collection? Explain your answer.

....

....

3 **a)** Write the following fractions and percentages as decimals:

i) $\frac{2}{5}$ .... **ii)** 35% .... **iii)** $\frac{1}{3}$ .... **iv)** 44% ....

b) Write these numbers in ascending order.

44% $\frac{2}{5}$ 35%   0.42 $\frac{1}{3}$ 0.25

....

....

4 **a)** Write the following as decimals: **i)** $\frac{4}{5}$ **ii)** 90% **iii)** $\frac{17}{20}$ **iv)** 85%

b) Write these numbers in descending order: $\frac{19}{20}$, 0.75, 90%, 0.92, $\frac{4}{5}$, 85%

5 **a)** Write the following as percentages: **i)** 0.62 **ii)** $\frac{3}{5}$ **iii)** 0.56 **iv)** $\frac{29}{50}$

b) Write the following numbers in ascending order: 61%, $\frac{3}{5}$, 0.56, 0.62, $\frac{29}{50}$, 65%

Ordering Numbers

1 Write the following numbers in order, starting with the smallest.

3   -5   -9   -2.3   1.5

2 Write the following numbers in order, starting with the smallest.

47.8   39.87   47.06   50   4.876

3 Write these in order, largest first.

$\frac{2}{3}$ $\frac{5}{8}$ $\frac{19}{24}$ $\frac{37}{48}$

4 Write these in order, largest first.

73% $\frac{4}{5}$ **0.7** $\frac{3}{4}$

5 Write in order, smallest first.

$\frac{11}{25}$ $\frac{15}{31}$ **0.467**   **48.6%** $\sqrt{0.4}$

6 Write in order, smallest first.

-6.78   **-8**   **$-\frac{20}{3}$**   **-6.49**

Everyday Maths

1 **a)** Alma buys a washing machine. The price is £380 + VAT at 17.5%.

What is the total cost of the washing machine?

....

....

b) The total cost of a home stereo system is £517 including VAT at 17.5%.

What is the price of the home stereo system before VAT?

....

....

2 **Mr Smith wants to invest £20 000 for 4 years. He has two options:**

SIMPLE INTEREST AT 5% PER ANNUM OR £7000 AT THE END OF 4 YEARS

Which option will make him the most money? Show all your working.

....

....

....

3 **Peter wants to buy a car. There are two payment options:**

Cash price: £8000 or Hire Purchase: 30% deposit + 24 monthly

payments of £255

a) What is the deposit required for hire purchase?

....

b) Calculate the percentage increase if Peter pays for the car by hire purchase compared with buying the

car at the cash price.

....

....

....

Everyday Maths

4 **Mr Spark receives an electricity bill. Complete the bill by filling in the gaps.**

Meter Reading				Amount (£)
Present	Previous	Units Used	Pence per unit	
32467	30277	a)	8p	b) ....
			Quarterly charge	9.60
			Total charged this quarter excluding VAT	c) ....
			VAT at 5%	d) ....
			Total payable	e) ....

5 **Use the timetable alongside to answer the following questions:**

a) Grace wants to arrive in London before midday. What is the latest train she can catch from Milford station to get there in time and how long will her train journey take?

....

....

b) Simon needs to get to Woking by 11.15am because he has a job interview. What is the time of the last train he can catch from Farncombe?

....

c) What percentage of trains departing from Woking station take less than 30 minutes to arrive at London Waterloo?

....

....

Petersfield, Milford, Farncombe, Woking to London Waterloo

Mondays to Fridays	AN	NW	AN	AN	AN
Petersfield	0752	0811	0833	0901	0928
Liphook					
Haslemere					
Witley					
Milford (Surrey)	0806	0829	0845	0917	0941
Godalming					
Farncombe	0822	0850	0900	0937	0959
Guildford					
Reading					
Woking	0830	0900	0907	0947	1007
Heathrow Airport (T1)					
Clapham Junction					
London Waterloo	0903	0932	0939	1018	1036

Mondays to Fridays	AN	NW	AN	AN	AN
Petersfield	0949	0956	1019	1049	1055
Liphook					
Haslemere					
Witley					
Milford (Surrey)	1002	1011	1032	1102	1114
Godalming					
Farncombe	1017	1032	1047	1117	1132
Guildford					
Reading					
Woking	1026	1043	1059	1128	1142
Heathrow Airport (T1)					
Clapham Junction					
London Waterloo	1052	1111	1125	1155	1211

6 What is the total cost of a vacuum cleaner if the price is £180 + VAT at 17.5%?

7 Mr Brum wants to buy a car costing £6000. He buys it on hire purchase paying £124 a month for 3 years. His total repayment is £6264. What percentage deposit did he pay?

8 Mr Plug receives an electricity bill. The cost per unit is 8p and the quarterly charge is £9.60. It says on his bill that the total payable for this quarter excluding VAT is £80.24. How many units has he used this quarter?

9 Using the timetable above, what is the difference between the average journey time of Peak time trains and the average journey time of Off Peak trains travelling from Petersfield to London Waterloo? Trains that arrive at London Waterloo after 10am are classified as Off Peak. Give your answer to 1 decimal place.

Ratio and Proportion

1 **Jim weighs 70kg. His sister Cathy weighs 35kg.**

  a) Calculate the ratio of Jim's weight to Cathy's weight.

  ....

  b) Express your answer to part a) in the form 1 : n. ....

2 **Freya is 90cm tall. Her brother Tom is 1.35m tall.**

  a) Calculate the ratio of Freya's height to Tom's height.

  ....

  b) Express your answer to part a) in the form 1 : n. ....

3 $\frac{3}{7}$ **of the teachers at a school are male.**

  a) What is the ratio of male teachers to female teachers?

  ....

  b) Express your answer to part a) in the form 1 : n. ....

4 **A large tin of baked beans costs 36p and weighs 450g. A small tin of baked beans costs 22p and weighs 250g.**

  a) Calculate the ratio of the weight of the two tins. ....

  b) Calculate the ratio of the cost of the two tins. ....

  c) Which tin represents the best value for money? Explain your choice.

  ....

  ....

5 **a)** Divide 80p in the ratio 2 : 3   **b)** Divide 6.3m in the ratio 2 : 3 : 4

  ....

  ....

  ....

6 **£5000 is shared between three women in the ratio of their ages. Their combined age is 120 years. If Susan gets £2500, Janet gets £1500 and Polly gets the remainder, what are their ages?**

  ....

  ....

  ....

  ....

  ....

Ratio and Proportion

7 In a maths class there are 30 pupils on the register and the ratio of girls to boys is 3 : 2. If 4 girls and 2 boys are absent from the class what does the ratio of girls to boys become?

....

....

....

....

8 A builder makes concrete by mixing cement, gravel, sand and water in the ratio 2 : 8 : 5 : 3 by weight. How many kilograms of sand, to the nearest kg, does he need to make 10 000kg of concrete?

....

....

....

....

9 Opposite is a recipe for making 10 biscuits.

Recipe
90g of flour
130g oatmeal
80g margarine

   a) Calculate the amount of each ingredient needed to make 25 biscuits.

   ....

   ....

   ....

   b) How many biscuits can be made using 0.715kg of oatmeal?

   ....

   ....

   ....

10 100ml of semi skimmed milk contains 4.8g carbohydrate and 1.8g fat.
   a) What is the ratio of carbohydrate to fat? **b)** Express your answer to part a) in the form 1 : n.

11 A large tub of margarine weighs 500g and costs £1.10. A small tub of margarine which normally weighs 250g has an extra 10% free and costs 52p. Which tub of margarine represents the best value for money? Explain.

12 Divide…
   a) 4.2cm in the ratio 1 : 2, **b)** 980g in the ratio 2 : 3 : 4 : 5

13 450 tickets were sold for a raffle at 20p each. The ratio of the cost of prizes to profit made is 5 : 13. How much profit did the raffle make?

14 The interior angles of a quadrilateral are in the ratio 2 : 3 : 5 : 8. What is the size of the largest angle?

15 A large packet of washing powder weighs 2.5kg and costs £5.60. How much should a 750g packet of washing powder cost if it represents the same value for money as the large packet?

Estimating and Checking

1 **a) i)** Without using a calculator estimate the answer to 106×53

....

ii) Work out the actual answer using a calculator. ....

b) i) Without using a calculator estimate the answer to 88×152

....

ii) Work out the actual answer using a calculator. ....

c) i) Without using a calculator estimate the answer to $\dfrac{29.4 \times 58}{19.6}$

....

ii) Work out the actual answer using a calculator. ....

d) i) Without using a calculator estimate the answer to 384×7.1

....

ii) Work out the actual answer using a calculator. ....

2 **John and Donna collect and keep all their loose change. The table below shows how much they collected for three successive months.**

MONTH	JOHN	DONNA
JUNE	£7.36	£9.10
JULY	£8.90	£16.58
AUGUST	£13.47	£4.52

a) John has calculated that he has collected £29.73 altogether.

i) Check by estimation whether he is likely to be correct.

....

ii) Check John's calculation for accuracy.

....

b) Donna has calculated that she has collected £31.20 altogether.

i) Check by estimation whether she is likely to be correct.

....

ii) Check Donna's calculation for accuracy.

....

3 Check the following calculations by estimation and then for accuracy. Finish by making any necessary corrections.
a) $13 + 29 + 43 = 82$ **b)** $9.06 + 11.58 + 7.23 + 13.86 = 41.73$
c) $(3 \times 6.25) + 92 - 10 = 101.75$ **d)** $(4.7 \times 6.3) + (0.8 \times 9.5) = 40.21$

Algebraic Expressions

1 Simplify…

a) $a + 2a$

....

b) $5x + 6x$

....

c) $11a - 6a$

....

d) $9p - 2p + 4p$

....

e) $2a^2 + 3a^2$

....

f) $10w^2 - w^2 + 2w^2$

....

g) $2a + 3b + 4a + 5b$

....

h) $7c - 8d - 9c + 10d$

....

i) $3a \times 2b$

....

j) $12pq \times 2r$

....

k) $4ab + 8cd - 7ab + cd + ab$

....

l) $-4x^2 + 6x + 7 + 3x^2 - 11x + 2$

....

m) $14 - 8p^2 + 11p + 2p^2 - 4p + 3$

....

The Rules of Indices

1 **Simplify...**

a) $a^2 \times a^3$

....

b) $4b^3 \times 3b$

....

c) $6p^4 \times 4p^6$

....

d) $r^6 \div r^2$

....

e) $12c^4 \div 3c^3$

....

f) $18a^2b \div 9a$

....

g) $15a^3b^2 \div 3ab$

....

2 **Simplify...**

a) $\dfrac{8ab^2}{4b}$

....

....

....

b) $\dfrac{16a^3b^2}{ab^2}$

....

....

....

c) $\dfrac{12bc^2 \times 3ab^2}{4abc}$

....

....

....

3 **Simplify...**
    a) $12x + 6x$ **b)** $12x - 6x$ **c)** $12x \times 6x$ **d)** $12x \div 6x$ **e)** $4p^2 - 11p^2$
    f) $19ab - 13bc + 2ab + 16bc$ **g)** $13ab + 4a^2b - 2ab^2 + 3a^2b - 4ab + 10ab^2$

4 **Simplify...**
    a) $a^4 \times a^3 \times a^2$ **b)** $2x^2 \times 3x \times 5x^5$ **c)** $16x^4 \div 16x^2$ **d)** $20a^3b^2c \div 10a^2b$

Substitution

1 If $p = 2$, $q = 5$ and $r = -4$, find the value of...

a) $2p + 3q$ ....

b) $2(p + q)$ ....

c) $2pq$ ....

d) p^2q ....

e) $pq - q^2$ ....

f) pqr ....

g) $p^3 + r^2$ ....

h) $\dfrac{4p}{r}$ ....

i) $p^2q^2 + \dfrac{r}{p}$ ....

j) $\dfrac{p}{q} + \dfrac{r}{q}$ ....

2 If $x = \frac{1}{2}$, $y = \frac{1}{3}$ and $z = -2$, find the value of...

a) $x + y$ ....

b) xz ....

c) xz^2 ....

d) $\frac{1}{x} + z$ ....

3 Find the value of...

a) $3x - 7$ when $x = -3$ ....

b) $4(x^2 - 1)$ when $x = -3$ ....

c) $4(x - 1)^2$ when $x = 5$ ....

d) $(x + 2)(x - 3)$ when $x = 6$ ....

e) $(x^2 - 5)(x + 8)$ when $x = -5$ ....

4 If $e = 3$, $f = 8$, $g = -4$ and $h = \frac{1}{4}$, find the value of...

a) ef **b)** fg **c)** gh **d)** $e + f + g$ **e)** $f + g + h$ **f)** $e^2 - f$ **g)** g^2h **h)** $f \div g$ **i)** $e^3 + g$ **j)** $2f \div g^2$ **k)** $\frac{1}{e} + h$ **l)** $e^2 + f + g^2$

5 Find the value of...

a) $5x^2 - 3$ when $x = -4$ **b)** $5(x - 3)$ when $x = -4$ **c)** $5x^2 - 3$ when $x = -2$ **d)** $(x + 3)(2x - 1)$ when $x = 2$

e) $(x^2 + 3)(x - 5)$ when $x = -1$

Brackets and Factorisation

1 **Expand and simplify...**

a) $4(2x + 1)$

b) $3(3r - 7)$

c) $2(3m + 2)$

d) $11(4 - 3x)$

e) $5(4x - 3y)$

f) $4(3 + p)$

g) $x(5 + 3x)$

h) $10(4x - 3)$

i) $x(4 - x)$

j) $5(-4 + x)$

k) $-3(2 + x)$

l) $3(-2 + 4p)$

m) $2p(4 - p)$

n) $6r(r - 3)$

o) $10x(4x - 3)$

p) $5(2y + 4) + 3$

q) $5(2 - 3x) + 7x$

r) $11(5 - 3x) - 9$

s) $10(3x - 4) - 9x$

t) $5(3 - 2x) + 7$

u) $4x(2x + 3) + 5x$

2 **Factorise the following expressions:**

a) $5x + 10$

b) $4x - 8$

c) $6x + 10y$

d) $5x^2 + 7x$

e) $8p + 13p^2$

f) $4a^2 - 5a$

g) $20ab + 5cd$

h) $10ab - 15bc$

i) $10x^2 + 5x$

3 **Expand and simplify...**
   a) $6(4x - y)$ **b)** $3x(2x + 5)$ **c)** $4x^2(2y - x)$ **d)** $6x(3 - x^2)$

4 **Factorise the following expressions:**
   a) $9x - 15$ **b)** $9x + 9$ **c)** $20x^2 - x$ **d)** $4x - 20x^3$

Linear Equations

1 **Solve the following equations:**

a) $5x = 35$

b) $3x + 4 = 16$

c) $5x + 8 = 23$

d) $4x - 7 = 5$

e) $10x - 8 = 12$

f) $8 + 3x = 29$

g) $2(x + 2) = 12$

h) $5(x - 3) = 10$

i) $4(5 + 3x) = 14$

j) $5x = 2x + 9$

k) $7x = 15 - 3x$

l) $2x = x - 8$

m) $11x + 3 = 3x + 7$

n) $5 + 7x = 23 + 3x$

o) $10x - 6 = 3x + 15$

p) $8(3x - 2) = 20$

q) $5(x + 7) = 3(9 + x)$

r) $8(4x - 6) = 7(3x - 10)$

2 **a)** Joan thinks of a number.

If you multiply it by 3 and add 12 the

answer is 27.

Let the number Joan thinks of be x.

Form an equation and then solve it.

b) Jim thinks of a number.

If you divide it by 4 and then add 11 the

answer is 13.

Let the number Jim thinks of be x.

Form an equation and then solve it.

Linear Equations

3 Maggie is x years old.   Nigel is twice Maggie's age.   Helen is 4 years older than Nigel.

a) Write down an expression in terms of x for their combined age.

....

....

b) Their total combined age is 64 years. Form an equation and solve it to find Helen's age.

....

....

4 ABC is a triangle:

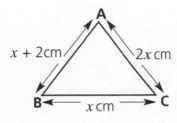

a) Write down an expression in terms of x for the perimeter of the triangle.

....

....

b) The perimeter of triangle ABC is 50cm. Form an equation and then solve it to find x.

....

....

5 ABCD is a rectangle:

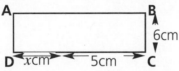

a) Write down an expression in terms of x for the area of the rectangle.

....

....

b) The area of rectangle ABCD is 72cm². Form an equation and then solve it to find x.

....

....

6 Solve the following equations to find the value of x:
   a) $2x + 5 = 17$ **b)** $15 + 3x = 3$ **c)** $4x = x + 18$ **d)** $10x = 7x - 15$ **e)** $4x - 3 = 6x + 12$ **f)** $9x + 7 = 4x - 13$
   g) $14 + 5x = 7x + 2$ **h)** $23 - 8x = x - 4$ **i)** $40x - 36 = 7x + 30$ **j)** $4(x + 5) = 36$ **k)** $7(2x - 3) = 14$ **l)** $6 = 4(3x - 9)$
   m) $16 = 4(11 - 5x)$ **n)** $5(x + 1) = 2(x + 7)$ **o)** $11(3x + 2) = 6x - 5$ **p)** $9(2x + 4) - 4(5x + 8) = 0$

7 Janice thinks of a number. If you subtract 6 from it and then multiply by 3 the answer is 21.
   Let the number that Janice thinks of be x. Form an equation and solve it to find the value of x.

8 For each of the following form an equation and solve it to find x.
   a)   **b)**   **c)**

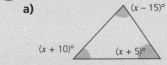 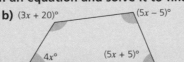 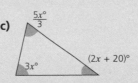

Formulae

1 Rearrange the following formulae to make x the subject:

a) $x + 4y = 3$

b) $6x + 7y = 50$

c) $7x - 5 = 3y$

d) $6y = 10 - 3x$

e) $x + 3y = 20$

f) $4x - 3 = 8y$

g) $5x + 3y = 3(6 - x)$

h) $4x - 5 = 3y$

i) $5x - 6y = 0$

j) $5x + 3 = 7y$

2 The circumference of a circle is given by the formula $2\pi r$. Calculate the circumference of the circle alongside if the radius is 4cm and $\pi = 3.14$

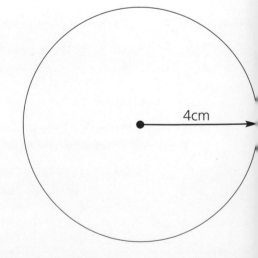

4cm

3 The distance travelled (*s*) by an object depends on its initial speed (*u*), its final speed (*v*) and the time of travel (*t*). It is given by the formula:

$$s = \left(\frac{u + v}{2}\right)t$$

Calculate the distance travelled in metres if initial speed = 4m/s, final speed = 12m/s and time = 5.5s

....

....

4 The formula that converts a temperature reading from degrees Celsius (°C) into degrees Fahrenheit (°F) is:

$$F = \frac{9}{5}C + 32$$

What is the temperature in degrees Fahrenheit if the temperature in degrees Celsius is 50°C?

....

....

....

5 The area of a circle is given by the formula $A = \pi r^2$.

a) If $\pi = 3.14$, calculate the area of a circle, which has a radius of 5cm, in cm².

....

....

....

b) If $\pi = 3.14$, use the above formula to work out the area of a circle, which has a radius of 40cm, in cm². Give your answer to two significant figures.

....

....

....

6 Rearrange the following formulae to make *p* the subject:
a) $4p - 3 = 4q$ **b)** $4 - 6p = q$ **c)** $2p + 15 = 11q$

7 The area of a parallelogram is given by the formula: Area = length × height. Calculate the area, in m², of a parallelogram that has length = 90cm and height = 1.2m

8 A garden centre buys shrubs at wholesale prices. They calculate the sale price (*s*), at which they are sold to customers, by increasing the wholesale price (*w*) by 50% and adding £2.50 per shrub.
a) Generate a formula for calculating the sale price of a shrub.
b) If the wholesale price of a shrub is £4.00, use your formula to calculate its sale price.

Trial & Improvement

1 The equation $x^3 - x = 15$ has a solution which lies between 2 and 3. By trial and improvement calculate a solution to 1 d.p.

x	$x^3 - x$	Comment
2	$2^3 - 2 = 8 - 2 = 6$	Less than 15
3	$3^3 - 3 = 27 - 3 = 24$	More than 15

Answer: ....

2 The equation $x^3 + 2x = 40$ has a solution which lies between 3 and 4. By trial and improvement calculate a solution to 2 d.p.

x	$x^3 + 2x$	Comment

Answer: ....

3 A rectangular box has the following dimensions:

x cm, x cm, $x + 3$cm

a) Show that the volume of the box is given by the expression $x^3 + 3x^2$.

....

b) The volume of the box is 40cm^3. Using trial and improvement, find x which has a value that lies between 2 and 3. Give your answer to 1 d.p.

x	$x^3 + 3x^2$	Comment

Answer: ....

4 a) The equation $x^3 + 10x = 24$ has one solution which lies between 1 and 2. Using trial and improvement, find the solution to 1 decimal place.

b) The equation $x^3 - 6x = 65$ has one solution which lies between 4 and 5. Using trial and improvement, find the solution to 2 decimal places.

5 A rectangular box has the following dimensions: length = $2x$ cm, width = x cm and height = $x + 3$cm.

a) Show that the volume of the box is given by the expression $2x^3 + 6x^2$.

b) The volume of the box is 50cm^3. Using trial and improvement find x, which has a value that lies between 2 and 3. Give your answer to 1 decimal place.

Sequences

1 a) The first four numbers of a sequence are:

1, 3, 7, 15...

The rule to continue this sequence of numbers is: **Multiply the previous number by 2 and then add 1**

i) What are the next two numbers in the sequence? ....

ii) The following sequence obeys the same rule:

-2, -3, -5, -9...

What are the next two numbers in this sequence? ....

b) The first four numbers of a sequence are:

3, 4, 6, 10...

The rule to continue this sequence of numbers is: **Subtract 1 from the previous number and then**

multiply by 2

i) What are the next two numbers in the sequence? ....

ii) The following sequence obeys the same rule:

1, 0, -2, -6...

What are the next two numbers in this sequence? ....

2 a) The first four square numbers are 1, 4, 9 and 16. What are the next four numbers in the sequence?

....

b) The first four triangular numbers are 1, 3, 6 and 10. What are the next four numbers in the sequence?

....

3 The nth term of a sequence is $5n + 8$.

a) What is the value of the 3rd term?

....

b) What is the value of the 10th term?

....

4 The nth term of a sequence is $2n - 11$.

a) What is the value of the 4th term?

....

b) What is the value of the 16th term?

....

5 The nth term of a sequence is $2n - 9$.

a) Which term has a value of 19?

....

b) Which term has a value of -5?

....

6 The nth term of a sequence is $7n + 6$.

a) Which term has a value of 69?

....

b) Which term has a value of 90?

....

Sequences

7 The first four terms of a sequence are:

3, 5, 7, 9, ...

Write down a formula for the *n*th term of this sequence and add a further 5 terms to the sequence.

....

....

8 The first four terms of a sequence are:

6, 4, 2, 0, ...

Write down a formula for the *n*th term of this sequence and add a further 5 terms to the sequence.

....

....

9 Here is a sequence of diagrams made up of squares:

Diagram 1   **Diagram 2**   **Diagram 3**   **Diagram 4**

a) Write down a formula for the number of squares (*s*) in terms of diagram number (*n*).

....

....

....

b) How many squares would there be in diagram 8?

....

c) Which number diagram would have 49 squares?

....

....

10 Here is a sequence of diagrams made up of circles.

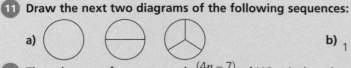

Diagram 1   **Diagram 2**   **Diagram 3**   **Diagram 4**

a) Write down a formula for the number of circles (*c*) in terms of diagram number (*n*).

....

....

b) How many circles would there be in diagram 15?

....

c) Which number diagram would have 81 circles?

....

---

11 Draw the next two diagrams of the following sequences:

a)

b)
```
                           1
              1          1   1
     1      1   1      1   2   1
1        1   2   1    1   3   3   1
```

12 The *n*th term of a sequence is $\frac{(4n-7)}{3}$ **a)** What is the value of the 10th term? **b)** Which term has a value of 27?

13 The first four terms of a sequence are: **15, 11, 7, 3...**

a) Write down a formula for the *n*th term of this sequence. **b)** What is the value of **i)** the 10th term? **ii)** the 100th term?

1 Write down the coordinates of all the plotted points below.

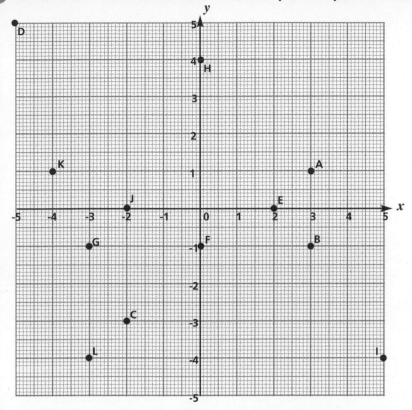

A (..................... , ...)

B (..................... , ...)

C (..................... , ...)

D (..................... , ...)

E (..................... , ...)

F (..................... , ...)

G (..................... , ...)

H (..................... , ...)

I (..................... , ...)

J (..................... , ...)

K (..................... , ...)

L (..................... , ...)

2 Use the axes below to help you answer the following questions:

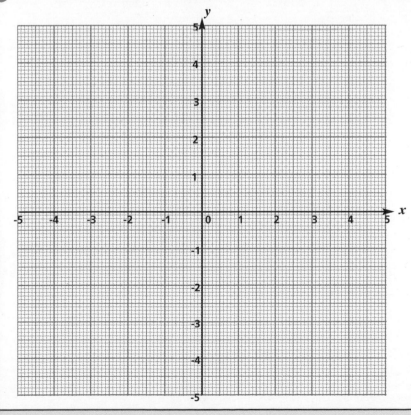

a) The coordinates of 3 points are A (3,0), B (0,-3), C (-3,0). What are the coordinates of point D if ABCD is a square?

....

b) The coordinates of 3 points are P (4,2), Q (3,-2), R (-2,-2). What are the coordinates of point S if PQRS is a parallelogram?

....

c) The coordinates of 3 points are E (1,5), F (4,4), G (1,-3). What are the coordinates of point H if EFGH is a kite?

....

3 The coordinates of 3 points are A (2,3), B (2,-2), C (-3,-2). What are the coordinates of point D if ABCD is a square?

4 The coordinates of 3 points are P (-4,0), Q (3,4), R (4,0). What are the coordinates of point S if PQRS is a kite?

Straight Line Graphs

1 **On the axes provided, draw and label the graphs of the following linear functions for values of x between -2 and 2:**

a) $y = 2x$

x	-2	0	2
y	-4	0	4

b) $y = 2x - 1$

x	-2	0	2
y	-5		

c) $y = x + 2$

x			
y			

d) $y = -2x$

x			
y			

e) $y = -x - 3$

x			
y			

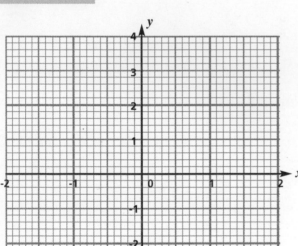

2 **a)** Make y the subject of the following function:

$2y - x = 8$

....

....

b) On the axes provided, draw and label the graph of the rearranged function from part a).

x			
y			

c) A point, which lies on the line of the graph that you have just drawn, has the coordinates $(5, p)$. Calculate the value of p.

....

....

d) Another point that lies on the line of the drawn graph has the coordinates $(q, 0)$. Calculate the value of q.

....

....

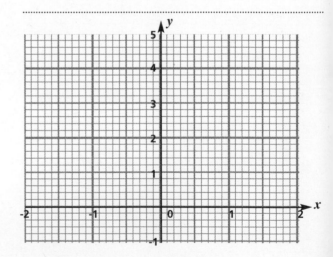

3 **a)** Make y the subject of the following function: $y - 3x = -4$
b) Draw the graph of the rearranged function for values of x between -3 and 3.
c) Use the graph to calculate the value of y if $x = 1.5$
d) Use the graph to calculate the value of x if $y = 3.2$

4 **a)** Draw graphs of $y = 3x$ and $y = x + 5$ for values of x between 0 and 4 on the same set of axes.
b) What is the x coordinate of the point where the two lines cross?
c) Now solve the equation $3x = x + 5$.

Straight Line Graphs

xy

1 Find the gradient and intercept of the following linear equations:

a) $y = 2x + 1$

....

....

....

b) $y = 3x - 1$

....

....

....

c) $x + y = 3$

....

....

....

d) $4y = 7 - 8x$

....

....

....

e) $2y - 2x = 9$

....

....

....

f) $2x = y - 2$

....

....

....

2 Four of the equations from question 1 have been plotted below. What is the equation of each line?

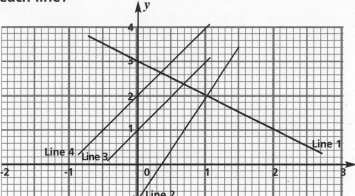

Line 1: ....

Line 2: ....

Line 3: ....

Line 4: ....

3 What is the equation of the line which crosses the *y*-axis at...

a) (0,1) and is parallel to $y = 2x$? ....

b) (0,1) and is parallel to $y = -2x$? ....

c) (0,-2) and is parallel to $y = 2x$? ....

d) (0,-2) and is parallel to $y = x + 2$? ....

e) (0,3) and is parallel to $y = -x - 3$? ....

f) (0,-3.5) and is parallel to $y = -x$? ....

---

4 Find the gradient and intercept of the following linear equations:
   a) $y = -3x - 3$ **b)** $4y = 3x + 8$ **c)** $2y - x = 3$ **d)** $x - 2y = 3$ **e)** $2y - 3 = x$ **f)** $\dfrac{y - 2x}{3} = 5$ **g)** $\dfrac{y - 4x}{5} = 1$

5 What is the equation of the line which crosses the *y*-axis at **a)** (0,4) and is parallel to $y = x - 4$, **b)** (0,0) and is perpendicular to $y = x - 4$

6 Which of the following linear functions would produce parallel lines if drawn on the same axes:
   i) $y = 2x + 3$ **ii)** $y + 2x = 3$ **iii)** $2y - 4x = 7$ **iv)** $y - 6 = 2x$

Straight Line Graphs

1 Find the gradient, intercept and equation of the following lines.

a)

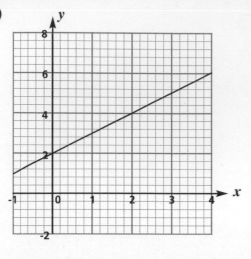

....
....
....
....

b)

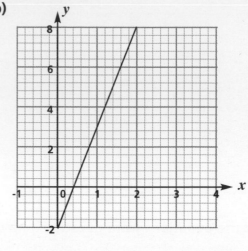

....
....
....
....

c)

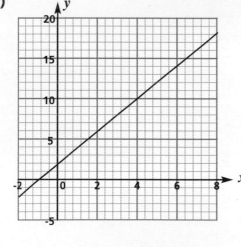

....
....
....
....

d)

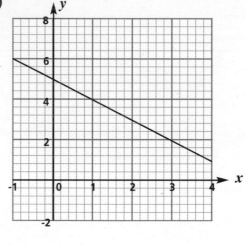

....
....
....
....

2 Plot the following points: A (0,1), B (4,5), C (1,4) and D (4,1).
a) Calculate the gradient of **i)** line AB, **ii)** line CD **b)** What is the equation of **i)** line AB, **ii)** line CD?

3 A line has intercept $c = +2$. A point with coordinates (4,4) lies on the line. What is the equation of the line?

4 A line has intercept $c = +5$. A point with coordinates (4,1) lies on the line. What is the equation of the line?

Straight Line Graphs

xy

1 On the axes below are the graphs of 6 lines. What is the equation of each line?

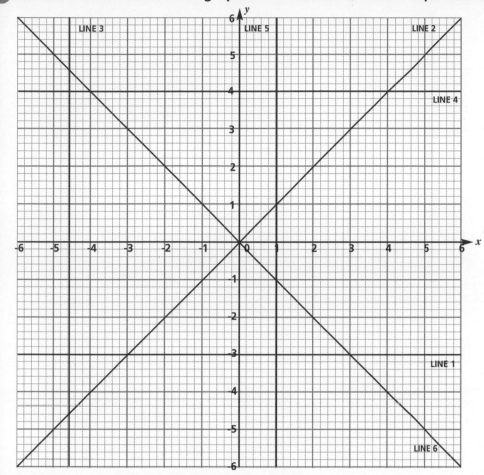

Line 1 ....

Line 2 ....

Line 3 ....

Line 4 ....

Line 5 ....

Line 6 ....

2 a) Two points lie on a line and have coordinates (-3,0) and (4,0).

What is the equation of the line? ....

b) Two points lie on a line and have coordinates (-1,5) and (-1,3).

What is the equation of the line? ....

c) Two points lie on a line and have coordinates (-4,4) and (4,-4).

What is the equation of the line? ....

3 What is the equation of the line that passes through the point with coordinates (3,3) and has a gradient of 1? ....

a) What are the coordinates of the point of intersection of the two lines $y = x$ and $y = -3$?

....

b) What are the coordinates of the point of intersection of the two lines $y = 6$ and $x = -2$?

....

5 What is the equation of the line that is parallel to the x-axis and passes through the point with coordinates (2.5, 3.6)?

6 What is the equation of the line that is perpendicular to the x-axis and passes through the point with coordinates (-2.8, 1.2)?

Linear Inequalities

1 Show the following inequalities on the number lines.

a) $x > 4$

b) $x \leqslant 5$

2 Solve the following inequalities and show the solutions on the number lines.

a) $x + 3 \geqslant 11$

b) $x - 4 < -7$

c) $2x \leqslant 12$

d) $\frac{x}{3} > 6$

3 x is an integer.

List the values of x that satisfy the following inequalities.

a) $3 \leqslant x \leqslant 7$

b) $-4 \leqslant x < 2$

---

4 Solve these inequalities.

a) $3x + 1 < 16$ **b)** $2x - 6 > -3$

5 List the integer values of x that satisfy these inequalities.

a) $-3 < x < 0$ **b)** $-9.2 < x < 7$

Graphs of Quadratic Functions

xy

1 Below is a table of values for $y = x^2 - 2$.

x	-2	-1	0	1	2
y	2	-1	-2	-1	2

a) Draw the graph of $y = x^2 - 2$.

b) From your graph find the value(s) of…

   i) y when $x = 1.5$

   ....

   ii) x when $y = 1.5$

   ....

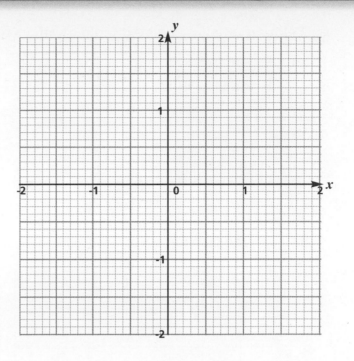

2 Below is a half completed table of values for $y = x^2 + x - 3$.

a) Complete the table.

x	-3	-2	-1	0	1	2
x^2		4		0		4
$+x$		-2		0		2
-3		-3		-3		-3
$y = x^2 + x - 3$		-1		-3		3

b) Draw the graph of $y = x^2 + x - 3$.

c) From your graph find the value(s) of…

   i) y when $x = -2.5$

   ....

   ii) x when $y = 1.6$

   ....

d) From your graph find the solutions to the equation $x^2 + x - 3 = 0$.

   ....

e) From your graph find the solutions to the equation $x^2 + x - 3 = 1$.

   ....

f) From your graph find the solutions to the equation $x^2 + x - 3 = -2$.

   ....

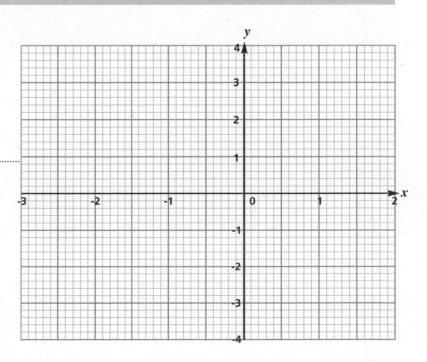

Graphs of Quadratic Functions

3 Below is a half completed table of values for $y = x^2 + 2x - 4$.

x	-4	-3	-2	-1	0	1	2
x^2		9		1		1	
$+2x$		-6		-2		2	
-4		-4		-4		-4	
$y = x^2 + 2x - 4$		-1		-5		-1	

a) Complete the table.

b) Draw the graph of $y = x^2 + 2x - 4$.

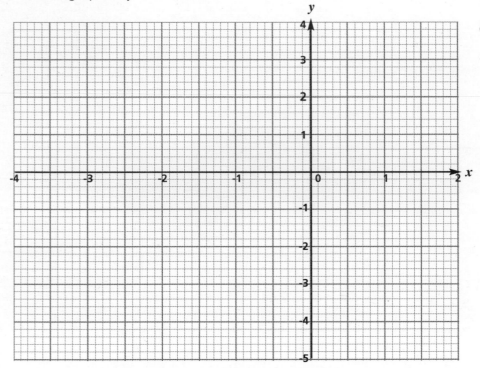

c) From your graph find the solutions to the equation $x^2 + 2x - 4 = 0$

....

....

....

....

....

4 Use your graph for question 3, above, to find the smallest value of $x^2 + 2x - 4$.

....

5 a) Draw a table of results for $y = x^2 + 4x - 6$ for values of x between -6 and 2.
   b) Draw the graph of $y = x^2 + 4x - 6$.
   c) From your graph find the solutions to the equation $x^2 + 4x - 6 = 0$

6 a) Draw the graph of $y = x^2 - 12$ for values of x between -4 and 4.
   b) From your graph find the Solutions to the equation $x^2 - 12 = 0$

7 a) Draw the graph of $y = x^2 - x - 8$ for values of x between -3 and 4.
   b) From your graph find the solutions to the equation $x^2 - x - 8 = 0$

Real Life Graphs

1 **Two towns A and B are 100 miles apart.**
Mr Brown lives in A and drives to B,
Mr Smith lives in B and drives to A, on the
same day, along the same route.
Using the graph opposite...

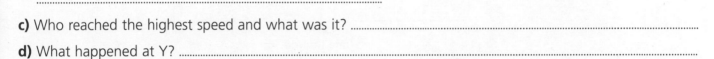

a) What time did Mr Smith set off?

....

b) Which motorist completed the journey in the
shortest time and what was that time?

....

c) Who reached the highest speed and what was it? ....

d) What happened at Y? ....

e) Who stopped and for how long? ....

2 **Here is part of a travel graph of Tina's**
journey to the shops and back.

a) Calculate Tina's speed in km/h for the first
20 mins. ....

....

b) Tina spends 20 mins at the shops, then
travels back home at 48km/h.
Complete her journey on the graph.

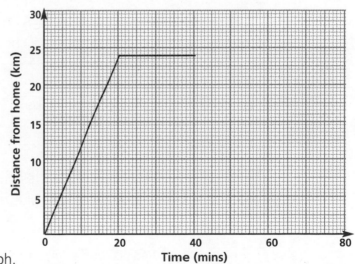

3 **a)** Plot the following data onto this speed-time graph.

Time (s)	0	1	2	3	4	5	6
Speed (m/s)	0	5	10	15	20	20	25

b) Between what times was the object travelling at a
steady speed?

....

....

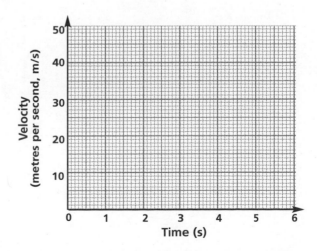

Real Life Graphs

4 **a)** A train leaves town A for town B at 1pm and maintains a steady speed of 60km/h. At 2pm another train leaves B for A maintaining a speed of 72km/h. The distance between A and B is 180km. Draw the distance-time graphs for these trains on the same axes.

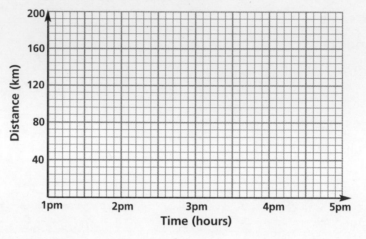

b) When do they pass each other?

....

5 **The cost of hiring a car is £30 plus an extra charge of 30p per mile.**

a) Complete this table:

Miles	0	10	20	30	50	100
Cost (£)	30	33				

b) On the axes below draw a graph to show the cost of hiring the car for up to 100 miles.

c) Use the graph to estimate how much it would cost to hire a car for a 52 mile journey.

....

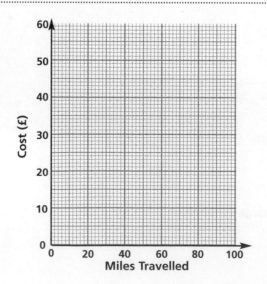

Real Life Graphs

6 These sketch graphs show the cost of running a business over several months. Identify which sketch matches each of these descriptions:

a) Costs are rising steadily. ....

b) Costs are falling after reaching a peak. ....

c) Costs are rising at an increasing rate. ....

d) Costs have been rising but are now levelling out. ....

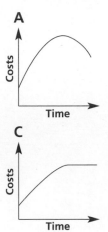

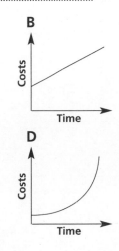

7 **a)** If £1 = $1.40 complete the table to convert pounds sterling (£) to US dollars ($).

Pounds (£)	10	20	30	40
US Dollars ($)				

b) On the axes opposite draw the graph to convert pounds (£) to US dollars ($).

c) Use your graph to convert $30 into pounds.

....

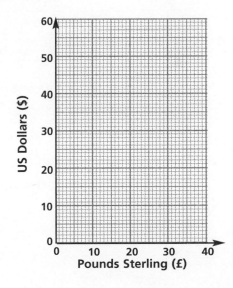

8 Three plumbers A, B and C charge as follows: A – Call out charge £20 then £10 per hour extra.
B – Call out charge £30 then £5 per hour extra.   C – Standard charge £50 regardless of time.

  a) Draw a graph for each plumber's charges on the same axes, for up to 5 hrs work.

  b) Which plumber is cheapest for a 30 minute job?

  c) Which plumber is cheapest for a $2\frac{1}{2}$ hour job?

  d) After what time will plumber C become the cheapest?

Angles

1 For each diagram work out the size of angle *p* and angle *q*, giving a reason for your answer. The diagrams are not drawn accurately.

a)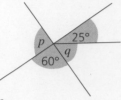

Angle *p* = ...

Reason: ....

....

Angle *q* = ...

Reason: ....

....

b)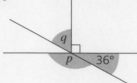

Angle *p* = ...

Reason: ....

....

Angle *q* = ...

Reason: ....

....

c)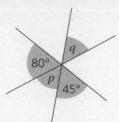

Angle *p* = ...

Reason: ....

....

Angle *q* = ...

Reason: ....

....

d)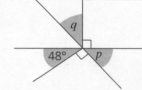

Angle *p* = ...

Reason: ....

....

Angle *q* = ...

Reason: ....

....

e)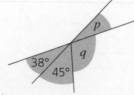

Angle *p* = ...

Reason: ....

....

Angle *q* = ...

Reason: ....

....

f)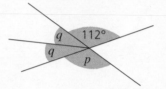

Angle *p* = ...

Reason: ....

....

Angle *q* = ...

Reason: ....

....

2 For each diagram work out the size of angle *c* and angle *d* giving a reason for your answer. The diagrams are not drawn accurately.

a)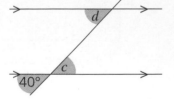

Angle *c* = ...

Reason: ....

....

Angle *d* = ...

Reason: ....

....

b)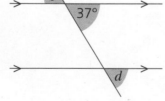

Angle *c* = ...

Reason: ....

....

Angle *d* = ...

Reason: ....

....

c)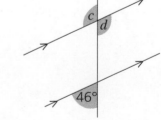

Angle *c* = ...

Reason: ....

....

Angle *d* = ...

Reason: ....

....

Angles

3 For each diagram work out the size of angle *m* and angle *n* giving a reason for your answer.

The diagrams are not drawn accurately.

a)

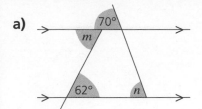

Angle *m* = ...

Reason: ....

....

Angle *n* = ...

Reason: ....

....

b)

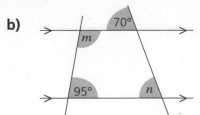

Angle *m* = ...

Reason: ....

....

Angle *n* = ...

Reason: ....

....

c)

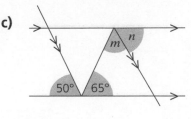

Angle *m* = ...

Reason: ....

....

Angle *n* = ...

Reason: ....

....

4 Work out the size of the angles marked *a*, *b* and *c*, giving reasons for your answer. The diagram is not drawn accurately.

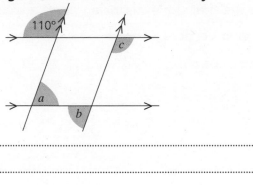

....

....

....

....

5 Work out the size of the angles marked *p*, *q*, *r* and *s*, giving reasons for your answer. The diagram is not drawn accurately.

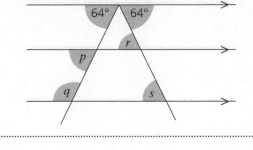

....

....

....

6 For each diagram work out the size of *x*. The diagrams are not drawn accurately.

a)

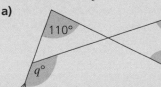

b)

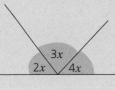

c)

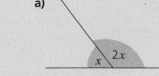

d)

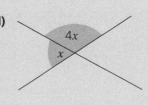

7 For each diagram work out the size of the angles marked giving reasons for your answer. The diagrams are not drawn accurately.

a)

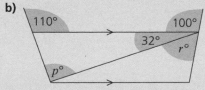

b)

c)

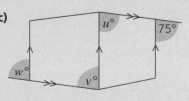

Triangles

1 Draw a diagram and write a short explanation to prove that the interior angles of a triangle add up to 180°.

....

....

....

....

....

2 Draw a diagram and write a short explanation to prove that the exterior angle of a triangle is equal to the sum of the interior angles at the other two vertices.

....

....

....

....

3 This diagram has six angles marked *a*, *b*, *c*, *d*, *e* and *f*.

a) Work out the size of angle *a* in terms of angle *b*.
b) Work out the size of angle *a* in terms of angles *d* and *f*.
c) Work out the size of angle *a* in terms of angles *c* and *e*.
d) What do angles *a*, *c* and *e* add up to?

Triangles

1 Below are four triangles. For each triangle work out the missing angle x and name the type of triangle giving a reason for your answer. The diagrams are not drawn accurately.

a)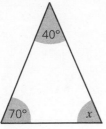

Angle x = ...

Type of Triangle:

....

Reason:

....

....

b)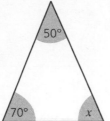

Angle x = ...

Type of Triangle:

....

Reason:

....

....

c)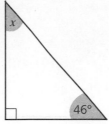

Angle x = ...

Type of Triangle:

....

Reason:

....

....

d)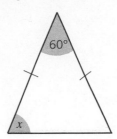

Angle x = ...

Type of Triangle:

....

Reason:

....

....

2 For each diagram below work out the size of angle p. The diagrams are not drawn accurately.

a)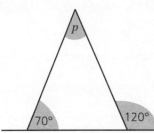

Angle p = ...

b)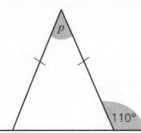

Angle p = ...

c)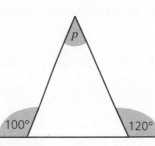

Angle p = ...

d)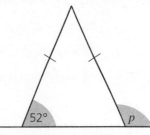

Angle p = ...

3 The diagram (opposite) shows a right-angled triangle ABC and an isosceles triangle CDE. Work out the size of the angles marked a and b giving reasons for your answers. The diagram is not drawn accurately.

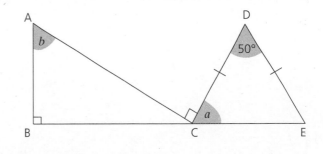

....

....

....

4 The diagram opposite shows an equilateral triangle ABC and a right-angled triangle CDE. Work out the size of the angles marked m and n giving reasons for your answers. The diagram is not drawn accurately.

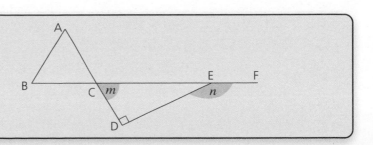

Quadrilaterals

1 Below are four quadrilaterals. For each quadrilateral work out the missing angle x and name the type of quadrilateral, giving a reason for your answer. They are not drawn to scale.

a)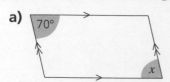

Angle x = ...

Type of Quadrilateral:

....

Reason:

....

....

b)

Angle x = ...

Type of Quadrilateral:

....

Reason:

....

....

c)

Angle x = ...

Type of Quadrilateral:

....

Reason:

....

....

d)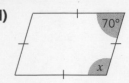

Angle x = ...

Type of Quadrilateral:

....

Reason:

....

....

2 Which type of quadrilateral am I?

a) I have diagonals that are not equal in length but they bisect each other at right-angles. They also bisect each of my interior angles. ....

b) I have diagonals that are equal in length and bisect each other. However they do not bisect each other at right-angles..

c) I have diagonals that are equal in length and bisect each other at right-angles. They also bisect each of my interior angles. ....

3 Draw a diagram and write a short explanation to prove that the interior angles of a quadrilateral add up to 360°.

....

....

....

....

4 Calculate the size of the labelled angles in the following diagrams. They are not drawn to scale.

a)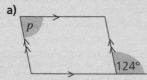

b)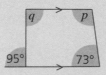

c)

d)

5 **a)** The interior angles of a quadrilateral are $x°$, $2x°$, $3x°$ and $4x°$. Work out the difference in size between the largest angle and the smallest angle in the quadrilateral.

b) The interior angles of a quadrilateral are $x + 20°$, $x - 30°$, $2x°$ and $110°$. Work out the size of x.

LONSDALE

REVISION PLUS

Edexcel
GCSE Mathematics
Foundation

Workbook Answers

Page 4
1. a) i) 7.3 ii) 7.32
   b) i) 16.8 ii) 16.78
   c) i) 0.02 ii) 0.018
   d) i) 0.1 ii) 0.105
   e) i) 7.1 ii) 7.07
2. Lowest: 68.35kg Highest: 68.45kg
3. Lowest: 1.645m Highest: 1.655m
4. a) i) 400 ii) 430
   b) i) 9000 ii) 9200
   c) i) 10 000 ii) 10 050
   d) i) 0.02 ii) 0.024
   e) i) 0.000 17 ii) 0.000 174
   f) i) 0.010 ii) 0.0104
5. 5749 − 5650 = 99
6. a) 135.7 b) 135.67 c) 100 d) 140 e) 136
7. a) 0.1 b) 0.06 c) 0.060 d) 0.06 e) 0.060 f) 0.0604
8. 47.64 − 47.55 = 0.09kg
9. a) 14.303 036 b) 14.3 (3 s.f.) or (1 d.p.)

Page 5
1. a) 102.5 b) 13.471 c)

	8	.	$^1/_{10}$	$^1/_{100}$	$^1/_{1000}$
			4	0	7

   d) 90.031 e)

100	10	1	.	$^1/_{10}$	$^1/_{100}$	$^1/_{1000}$
4	2	3		0	0	8

2. a) 0.6667 b) 0.4000 c) 0.0909 d) 0.7778
3. 0.306, 0.36, 0.63, 3.6, 6.3
4. a) 21.39 b) 108.037 c) 32.46 d) 717.21
5. a) 0.3750 b) 0.2222 c) 0.0333 d) 0.8800 e) 0.2667
6. 143.2, 14.32, 14.23, 13.42, 1.432, 1.342
7. £4.91
8. 28.16kg

Page 6
1. a) 47 b) 132.46 c) 0.146 d) 136 300 e) 98.28 f) 10.856
   g) 286.488 h) 7.35228
2. a) 97.2 b) 9.72 c) 9.72 d) 0.972 e) 0.0972
3. a) 195.657 b) 19 565 700 c) 195 657 d) 19 565.7
4. a) 156.7 b) 1.01 c) 3467.1 d) 25.52 e) 8.406 f) 358.19
   g) 3.0659 h) 0.0282
5. a) 16 544 b) 165.44 c) 1.6544 d) 0.16544
6. £109.97
7. £47
8. €39.92

Page 7
1. a) 1.63 b) 0.0347 c) 146.324 d) 0.001 246 7 e) 4.7 f) 34.2
   g) 4964 h) 458
2. a) 13 b) 0.13 c) 130 d) 0.013 e) 13
3. a) 34 b) 270 c) 3.4 d) 2.7 e) 0.27
4. a) 0.7162 b) 0.000 034 c) 0.4731 d) 78.6 e) 17.6 f) 67.6
5. a) 173 b) 17 300 c) 3.4 d) 58.82
6. 60 tickets
7. 14 days

Page 8
1. a) 4, 6, 20 b) 4, 20 c) 3, 15 d) 3, 6, 7, 21 e) 7, 21, f) 4, 6, 20
   g) 3, 7, 11 h) 4
2. a) 5, 11, 19, 31, 47, 81 b) 8, 24, 36 c) 5, 11, 22 d) 24, 36, 81
   e) 8, 24, 36 f) 5, 11, 19, 31, 47 g) 36, 81
3. a) $\frac{1}{8}$, 0.125 b) $\frac{1}{25}$, 0.04 c) 2 d) $\frac{4}{3}$, 1.$\dot{3}$
4. 10
5. a) $2^2 \times 3^2$ b) 2^6 c) $2 \times 3 \times 5 \times 31$

Page 9
6. a) 4 and 180 b) 4 and 1600
   c) 3 and 90 d) 2 and 1160
7. a) 3 and 120 b) 3 and 360
8. a) 12 and 20 b) 15, 30, 45
9. a) i) 25, 50, 100 ii) 25, 50, 100 iii) 14, 70, 84 iv) 29, 41, 61 b) 50
10. a) $\frac{1}{100}$, 0.01 b) 100 c) 100 d) $\frac{100}{99}$, 8$\frac{1}{99}$, 1.$\dot{0}\dot{1}$
11. a) $2 \times 3 \times 5$ b) $2^2 \times 5^2$ c) 2^{11}
12. a) 3, 90 b) 2, 1160 c) 3, 360

Page 10
1. a) 503 b) 28 009 c) 139 d) 41 449 e) 15 228 f) 428 155 g) 38
   h) 257 i) 4100 j) 573 000 k) 42.3 l) 0.008
2. a) 234 b) 8

3. a) 10^5 (100 000) b) 10^5 (100 000)
4. a) 4000 b) 5165 c) 3582 d) 4293 e) 31 691 f) 154 875 g) 367
   h) 2076 i) 9400 j) 40 300 k) 11 000 l) 339 420 000 m) 40.8 n) 0.55
   o) 0.06 p) 3.3942
5. a) 230 b) 10^2 (100)

Page 11
1. a) -11, -7, -3, -1, 2, 5, 12, 14 b) 467, 165, 70, 8, -62, -162, -230, -320
2. a) i) 8 ii) -4 iii) -5 iv) 5 v) 8 vi) -8 vii) -2 viii) -4 ix) -1 x) 6 xi) -4 xii) -5
   b) i) 12 ii) -8 iii) -16 iv) -6 v) -28 vi) 2
   c) i) -15 ii) 16 iii) 5 iv) -4 v) 1
   d) Many possible answers
3. a) −, = b) +, −, = c) ×, ÷, = d) ÷, +, =, or +, x, = e) −, +, ÷, =
   f) +, −, −, =, or −, −, x, =

Page 12
4. a) i) 17°C ii) 31°C iii) 4°C b) 11°C
5. a) £147.30 b) £260.00
6. -36, -11, -3, -1, 0, 3, 4, 19, 74, 100
7. a) -2 b) -8 c) 0 d) 300 e) -90 f) 20 g) -25
8. a) 15 b) -11 c) 19 d) -16 e) -11

Page 13
1. a) 8 b) 9 c) 64 d) 1000 e) 125 f) 36
2. a) 25, 64, 196 b) 27, 64, 125 c) 64 d) 64 e) 64 f) 80
3. a) 5 b) 3 c) 12 d) 11 e) 7 f) 1 g) 2 h) 6 i) 343
4. a) 4, 36, 64 b) 8, 27, 64 c) 64 d) 10 e) 36
5. a) 100 b) 1000 c) 10 000 d) 100 000 e) 1 000 000 f) 10 000 000
6. 10^8

Page 14
7. a) 9 b) -27 c) 25 d) -125 e) 1 f) -1
8. a) $2^5 = 32$ b) $3^3 = 27$ c) $4^6 = 4096$ d) $2^1 = 2$ e) $10^2 = 100$
   f) $6^4 = 1296$ g) 1 h) 2
9. a) 3^4 b) 2^7 c) 4^5
10. a) 5 b) 6 c) 12 d) 14 e) 4 f) 1 g) 2 h) 10 i) 3
11. a) 4^2 b) 3^2 c) 2^4
12. a) 64 b) 4 c) 256 d) 1600 e) 91 f) 132 g) 27 h) 16 i) 5
13. 3^7
14. a) 13 b) 5 c) 9 d) 5 e) 15
15. a) 27 b) 4

Page 15
1. a) 17 b) 67 c) 44 d) 11 e) 11 f) 1 g) 200 h) 20 i) -16
2. a) $(13 − 3) \times 4 + 3$ b) $13 − 3 \times (4 + 3)$ c) $(13 − 3) \times (4 + 3)$
   d) $13 − (3 \times 4) + 3$ e) $(3 \times 1.4 + 4) \times 2.5$ f) $7 + 3.2 \times (6 − 4.4)$
3. a) 43 b) -1 c) -35 d) 11 e) 12 f) 10 g) -1.5 h) -35
4. a) $3^2 − (4 \times 5) + 10$ b) $(3^2 − 4) \times 5 + 10$ c) $3^2 − 4 \times (5 + 10)$
5. a) $(4^2 − 3) \times 4 + 2$ b) $4^2 − 3 \times (4 + 2)$ c) $4^2 − (3 \times 4) + 2$

Page 16
1. a) 9 b) 20 c) 54 d) 44, 12 e) 160, 64 f) 84, 75
2. a) 3 b) 2 c) 2 d) 8, 3 e) 8, 2 f) 18, 7
3. a) > b) > c) > d) > e) > f) <
4. a) $\frac{16}{40}$, $\frac{40}{100}$, $\frac{10}{25}$ b) $\frac{35}{50}$, $\frac{28}{40}$, $\frac{84}{120}$
5. a) $\frac{9}{10}$, b) 7 c) $\frac{4}{5}$, d) $\frac{27}{46}$

Page 17
6. a) $\frac{1}{2}$, $\frac{3}{5}$, $\frac{2}{3}$, $\frac{11}{15}$, $\frac{5}{6}$ b) $\frac{9}{10}$, $\frac{5}{8}$, $\frac{3}{5}$, $\frac{1}{4}$, $\frac{9}{40}$
7. $\frac{22}{30}$, $\frac{23}{30}$, $\frac{24}{30}$ (Accept any two correct)
8. a) i) $2\frac{1}{5}$ ii) $2\frac{1}{6}$ iii) $4\frac{4}{5}$ iv) $10\frac{2}{3}$
   b) i) $\frac{10}{3}$ ii) $\frac{21}{4}$ iii) $\frac{58}{5}$ iv) $\frac{401}{20}$
9. a) $\frac{4}{6}$, $\frac{6}{9}$, $\frac{8}{12}$, $\frac{10}{15}$, etc. b) $\frac{8}{14}$, $\frac{12}{21}$, $\frac{16}{28}$, etc.
   c) $\frac{9}{11}$, $\frac{18}{22}$, $\frac{27}{33}$, $\frac{36}{44}$, etc. (Accept any three correct for each)
10. $\frac{1}{2}$, $\frac{3}{4}$, $\frac{4}{5}$, $\frac{9}{10}$, $\frac{19}{20}$
11. Accept any three fractions between $\frac{4}{5}$ and $\frac{9}{10}$, e.g. $\frac{17}{20}$, $\frac{25}{30}$, $\frac{26}{30}$, $\frac{41}{50}$, etc.

Page 18

1. **a)** $1\frac{5}{12}$ **b)** $1\frac{7}{72}$ **c)** $7\frac{2}{5}$ **d)** $11\frac{23}{24}$ **e)** $\frac{2}{5}$ **f)** $\frac{1}{5}$ **g)** $3\frac{17}{40}$ **h)** $4\frac{17}{30}$

2. $\frac{1}{3}$

3. **a)** $\frac{1}{10}$ **b)** $\frac{9}{35}$ **c)** $\frac{5}{6}$ **d)** $1\frac{1}{2}$ **e)** $\frac{3}{10}$ **f)** $\frac{5}{28}$ **g)** $\frac{3}{4}$ **h)** 2 **i)** $3\frac{5}{9}$ **j)** $\frac{7}{30}$

4. **a)** $1\frac{13}{40}$ **b)** $6\frac{17}{24}$ **c)** $\frac{7}{30}$ **d)** $\frac{4}{5}$ **e)** $\frac{7}{25}$ **f)** $1\frac{1}{12}$ **g)** $22\frac{1}{2}$ **h)** $\frac{7}{18}$

Page 19

1. £30

2. **a)** £5200 **b)** £162.50 **c)** $\frac{11}{20}$

3. **a)** £78.00 **b)** £145.80

4. $\frac{5}{6}$

5. **a) i)** £300 **ii)** £225 **b)** £400

6. $\frac{1}{90}$

Page 20

1. **a)** 12p **b)** 1.95km
2. **a)** 20% **b)** 5%
3. **a) i)** 0.54m **ii)** 45% **b) i)** 24kg **ii)** 60%
4. 12.5%
5. **a)** £1.17 **b)** 5.12kg **c)** £0.52
6. **a)** 66.6% or 66.7% (1 d.p.) **b)** 0.1% **c)** 27.5%
7. 30%
8. 17.5%

Page 21

1. £11 550
2. 34 450
3. **a)** £145 200 **b)** £132 300
4. **a)** £8000 **b)** £7200
5. No, 10% off discounted price rather than original price = £72
6. 247.5g

Page 22

1. 40 mins
2. £144
3. £4500
4. 220km
5. £60 000
6. £124
7. £3200
8. 300 stamps

Page 23

1. **a)** 0.3, 30% **b)** $\frac{9}{20}$, 45% **c)** $\frac{3}{8}$, 0.375 **d)** $0.\dot{6}$, $66.\dot{6}\%$ **e)** $\frac{1}{8}$, 12.5% **f)** $\frac{21}{25}$, 0.84 **g)** 1.8, 180% **h)** $4\frac{3}{5}$, 460% **i)** $2\frac{1}{4}$, 2.25

2. $\frac{3}{5}$ = 60%, more than 55%

3. **a) i)** 0.4 **ii)** 0.35 **iii)** $0.\dot{3}$ **iv)** 0.44 **b)** 0.25, $\frac{1}{3}$, 35%, $\frac{2}{5}$, 0.42, 44%

4. **a) i)** 0.8 **ii)** 0.9 **iii)** 0.85 **iv)** 0.85 **b)** $\frac{19}{20}$, 0.92, 90%, 85%, $\frac{4}{5}$, 0.75

5. **a) i)** 62% **ii)** 60% **iii)** 56% **iv)** 58% **b)** 0.56, $\frac{29}{50}$, $\frac{3}{5}$, 61%, 0.62, 65%

Page 24

1. -9, -5, -2.3, 1.5, 3
2. 4.876, 39.87, 47.06, 47.8, 50
3. $\frac{5}{8}$, $\frac{2}{3}$, $\frac{37}{48}$, $\frac{19}{24}$
4. $\frac{4}{5}$, $\frac{3}{4}$, 73%, 0.7.
5. $\frac{11}{25}$, 0.467, $\frac{15}{31}$, 48.6%, $\sqrt{0.4}$
6. -8, -6.78, $-\frac{20}{3}$, -6.49

Page 25

1. **a)** £446.50 **b)** £440
2. Simple Interest = £24 000, Lump Sum = £27 000 (Lump sum better value)
3. **a)** £2400 **b)** 6.5% increase

Page 26

4. **a)** 2190 **b)** £175.20 **c)** £184.80 **d)** £9.24 **e)** £194.04
5. **a)** 11:02, 53 mins **b)** 10:47 **c)** 60%
6. £211.50
7. 30%
8. 883 units
9. 2 mins

Page 27

1. **a)** 70 : 35 = 2 : 1 **b)** 1 : 0.5
2. **a)** 90 : 135 = 2 : 3 **b)** 1 : 1.5
3. **a)** 3 : 4 **b)** $1 : \frac{4}{3}$ or $1 : 1.\dot{3}$
4. **a)** 9 : 5 **b)** 18 : 11 **c)** Large tin is better value at 8p per 100g, compared with 8.8p per 100g for the smaller tin.
5. **a)** 32p : 48p **b)** 140cm : 210cm : 280cm or 1.4m : 2.1m : 2.8m
6. Susan – 60 years old, Janet – 36 years old, Polly – 24 years old

Page 28

7. 14 : 10 or 7 : 5
8. 2778kg
9. **a)** 225g flour, 325g oatmeal, 200g margarine **b)** 55 biscuits
10. **a)** 4.8 : 1.8 or 8 : 3 **b)** $1 : \frac{3}{8}$ or 1 : 0.375
11. Small tub is better value at 18.9p per 100g, compared with 22p per 100g.
12. **a)** 1.4cm : 2.8cm **b)** 140g : 210g : 280g : 350g
13. £65
14. 160°
15. £1.68

Page 29

1. **a) i)** 100 × 50 = 5000 **ii)** 5618
   b) i) 90 × 150 = 13500 **ii)** 13 376
   c) i) $\frac{30 \times 60}{20}$ = 90 **ii)** 87
   d) i) 400 × 7 = 2800 **ii)** 2726.4
2. **a) i)** 7 + 9 + 13 = £29 **ii)** £29.73 John, accurate
   b) i) 9 + 17 + 5 = £31 **ii)** £30.20 Donna, inaccurate
3. **a)** 10 + 30 + 40 = 80, answer = 85 (inaccurate)
   b) 9 + 12 + 7 + 14 = 42, answer = 41.73 (accurate)
   c) (3 × 6) + 90 – 10 = 98, answer = 100.75 (inaccurate)
   d) (5 × 6) + (1 × 10) = 40, answer = 37.21 (inaccurate)

Page 30

1. **a)** $3a$ **b)** $11x$ **c)** $5a$ **d)** $11p$ **e)** $5a^2$ **f)** $11w^2$ **g)** $6a + 8b$ **h)** $2d – 2c$ **i)** $6ab$ **j)** $24pqr$ **k)** $9cd – 2ab$ **l)** $9 – x^2 – 5x$ **m)** $17 – 6p^2 + 7p$

Page 31

1. **a)** a^5 **b)** $12b^4$ **c)** $24p^{10}$ **d)** r^4 **e)** $4c$ **f)** $2ab$ **g)** $5a^2b$
2. **a)** $2ab$ **b)** $16a^2$ **c)** $9b^2c$
3. **a)** $18x$ **b)** $6x$ **c)** $72x^2$ **d)** 2 **e)** $-7p^2$ **f)** $21ab + 3bc$
   g) $9ab + 7a^2b + 8ab^2$
4. **a)** a^9 **b)** $30x^8$ **c)** x^2 **d)** $2abc$

Page 32

1. **a)** 19 **b)** 14 **c)** 20 **d)** 20 **e)** -15 **f)** -40 **g)** 24 **h)** -2 **i)** 98 **j)** $\frac{-2}{5}$
2. **a)** $\frac{5}{6}$ **b)** -1 **c)** 2 **d)** 0
3. **a)** -16 **b)** 32 **c)** 64 **d)** 24 **e)** 60
4. **a)** 24 **b)** -32 **c)** -1 **d)** 7 **e)** $4\frac{1}{4}$ **f)** 1 **g)** 4 **h)** -2 **i)** 23 **j)** 1 **k)** $\frac{7}{12}$ **l)** 33
5. **a)** 77 **b)** -35 **c)** 17 **d)** 15 **e)** -24

Page 33

1. **a)** $8x + 4$ **b)** $9r – 21$ **c)** $6m + 4$ **d)** $44 – 33x$ **e)** $20x – 15y$
   f) $12 + 4pq$ **g)** $5x + 3x^2$ **h)** $40x – 30$ **i)** $4x – x^2$ **j)** $-20 + 5x$ or $5x – 20$
   k) $-6 – 3x$ **l)** $-6 + 12p$ **m)** $8p – 2p^2$ **n)** $6r^2 – 18r$ **o)** $40x^2 – 30x$
   p) $10y + 23$ **q)** $10 – 8x$ **r)** $46 – 33x$ **s)** $21x – 40$ **t)** $22 – 10x$
   u) $8x^2 + 17x$
2. **a)** $5(x + 2)$ **b)** $4(x – 2)$ **c)** $2(3x + 5y)$ **d)** $x(5x + 7)$ **e)** $p(8 + 13p)$
   f) $a(4a – 5)$ **g)** $5(4ab + cd)$ **h)** $5b(2a – 3c)$ **i)** $5x(2x + 1)$
3. **a)** $24x – 6y$ **b)** $6x^2 + 15x$ **c)** $8x^2y – 4x^3$ **d)** $18x – 6x^3$
4. **a)** $3(x – 5)$ **b)** $9(x + 1)$ **c)** $x(20x – 1)$ **d)** $4x(1 – 5x^2)$

Page 34
1. **a)** $x = 7$ **b)** $x = 4$ **c)** $x = 3$ **d)** $x = 3$ **e)** $x = 2$ **f)** $x = 7$ **g)** $x = 4$

 h) $x = 5$ **i)** $x = -0.5$ **j)** $x = 3$ **k)** $x = 1.5$ **l)** $x = -8$ **m)** $x = \frac{1}{2}$ or $x = 0.5$

 n) $x = 4.5$ **o)** $x = 3$ **p)** $x = 1\frac{1}{2}$ or $x = 1.5$ **q)** $x = -4$ **r)** $x = -2$

2. **a)** $3x + 12 = 27$, $x = 5$ **b)** $\frac{x}{4} + 11 = 13$, $x = 8$

Page 35
3. **a)** $x + 2x + 2x + 4 = 5x + 4$ **b)** $5x + 4 = 64$, $x = 12$, Helen is 28 years old
4. **a)** $4x + 2$cm **b)** $4x + 2 = 50$, $x = 12$cm
5. **a)** $6(x + 5)$ **b)** $6(x + 5) = 72$, $x = 7$cm
6. **a)** $x = 6$ **b)** $x = -4$ **c)** $x = 6$ **d)** $x = -5$ **e)** $x = -7.5$ **f)** $x = -4$ **g)** $x = 6$
 h) $x = 3$ **i)** $x = 2$ **j)** $x = 4$ **k)** $x = 2.5$ **l)** $x = 3.5$ **m)** $x = 1.4$ **n)** $x = 3$
 o) $x = -1$ **p)** $x = 2$
7. $3(x - 6) = 21$, $x = 13$
8. **a)** $3x = 180°$, $x = 60°$ **b)** $17x + 20° = 360°$, $x = 20°$
 c) $\frac{20x}{3} + 20° = 180°$, $x = 24°$

Page 36
1. **a)** $x = 3 - 4y$ **b)** $x = \frac{50 - 7y}{6}$ **c)** $x = \frac{3y + 5}{7}$ **d)** $x = \frac{10 - 6y}{3}$

 e) $x = 20 - 3y$ **f)** $x = \frac{8y + 3}{4}$ **g)** $x = \frac{18 - 3y}{8}$ **h)** $x = \frac{3y + 5}{4}$

 i) $x = \frac{6y}{5}$ **j)** $x = \frac{7y - 3}{5}$
2. $C = 25.12$cm

Page 37
3. $s = 44$m
4. $122°$F
5. **a)** $A = 78.5$cm² **b)** $A = 5000$cm² (2 s.f.)
6. **a)** $p = \frac{4q + 3}{4}$ **b)** $p = \frac{4 - q}{6}$ **c)** $p = \frac{11q - 15}{2}$
7. $A = 1.08$m²
8. **a)** $s = 1.5w + 2.5$ **b)** £8.50

Page 38
1. $x = 2.6$
2. $x = 3.23$
3. **a)** $x^2(x + 3) = x^3 + 3x^2$ **b)** 2.7cm
4. **a)** $x = 1.8$ **b)** $x = 4.52$
5. **a)** $2x(x)(x + 3) = 2x^3 + 6x^2$ **b)** $x = 2.2$cm

Page 39
1. **a) i)** 31, 63 **ii)** -17, -33 **b) i)** 18, 34 **ii)** -14, -30
2. **a)** 25, 36, 49, 64 **b)** 15, 21, 28, 36
3. **a)** 23 **b)** 58
4. **a)** -3 **b)** 21
5. **a)** 14th **b)** 2nd
6. **a)** 9th **b)** 12th

Page 40
7. $2n + 1$; 11, 13, 15, 17, 19
8. $-2n + 8$ or $8 - 2n$; -2, -4, -6, -8, -10
9. **a)** $s = 4n - 3$ **b)** 29 **c)** 13th
10. **a)** $c = 3n$ **b)** 45 **c)** 27th
11. **a)**

 b)
```
      1                 1
     1 1               1 1
    1 2 1             1 2 1
   1 3 3 1           1 3 3 1
  1 4 6 4 1         1 4 6 4 1
                   1 5 10 10 5 1
```
12. **a)** 11 **b)** 22nd
13. **a)** $-4n + 19$ **b) i)** -21 **ii)** -381

Page 41
1. **A** (3,1) **B** (3,-1) **C** (-2,-3) **D** (-5,5) **E** (2,0) **F** (0,-1) **G** (-3,-1) **H** (0,4)
 I (5,-4) **J** (-2,0) **K** (-4,1) **L** (-3,-4)
2. **a)** D (0,3) **b)** S (-1,2) **c)** H (-2,4)
3. D (-3,3)
4. S (3,-4)

Page 42
1. See p.8 for graphs

2. **a)** $y = \frac{x + 8}{2}$ or $\frac{x}{2} + 4$ **b)** See p.8 for graphs **c)** $p = 6.5$ **d)** $q = 4$
3. **a)** $y = 3x - 4$ **b)** See p.8 for graphs **c)** $y = 0.5$ **d)** $x = 2.4$
4. **a)** See p.8 for graphs **b)** $x = 2.5$ **c)** $x = 2.5$

Page 43
1. **a)** Gradient +2, intercept +1 **b)** Gradient +3, intercept -1
 c) Gradient -1, intercept +3 **d)** Gradient -2, intercept +1.75
 e) Gradient +1, intercept +4.5 **f)** Gradient +2, intercept +2
2. Line 1: $y = 3 - x$ or $x + y = 3$, Line 2: $y = 3x - 1$, Line 3: $y = 2x + 1$,
 Line 4: $y = 2x + 2$
3. **a)** $y = 2x + 1$ **b)** $y = -2x + 1$ **c)** $y = 2x - 2$ **d)** $y = x - 2$
 e) $y = x + 3$ or $x + y = 3$
 f) $y = -x - 3.5$ or $x + y = -3.5$
4. **a)** Gradient -3, intercept -3 **b)** Gradient $\frac{3}{4}$, intercept +2

 c) Gradient $+\frac{1}{2}$, intercept +1.5 **d)** Gradient $+\frac{1}{2}$, intercept -1.5

 e) Gradient $+\frac{1}{2}$, intercept +1.5 **f)** Gradient +2, intercept +15
 g) Gradient -4, intercept +5
5. **a)** $y = x + 4$ **b)** $y = -x$
6. i), iii) and iv)

Page 44
1. **a)** Gradient +1, intercept +2, $y = x + 2$ **b)** Gradient +5, intercept -2,
 $y = 5x + 2$ **c)** Gradient +2, intercept +2, $y = 2x + 2$
 d) Gradient -1, intercept +5, $y = -x + 5$
2. **a) i)** +1 **ii)** -1 **b) i)** $y = x + 1$ **ii)** $y = -x + 5$
3. $y = \frac{1}{2}x + 2$
4. $y = -x + 5$

Page 45
1. Line 1: $y = -3$, Line 2: $y = x$, Line 3: $x = -4.6$, Line 4: $y = 4$,
 Line 5: $x = 1$, Line 6: $y = -x$
2. **a)** $y = 0$ **b)** $x = -1$ **c)** $y = x$ or $x + y = 0$
3. $y = x$
4. **a)** (-3,-3) **b)** (-2,6)
5. $y = 3.6$
6. $x = -2.8$

Page 46
1. **a)** $x > 4$

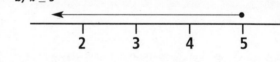

 b) $x \leq 5$

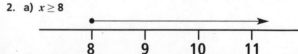

2. **a)** $x \geq 8$

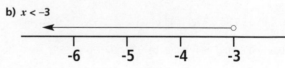

 b) $x < -3$

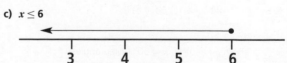

 c) $x \leq 6$

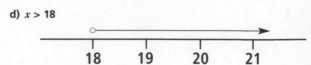

 d) $x > 18$

3. **a)** 3, 4, 5, 6, 7 **b)** -4, -3, -2, -1, 0, 1
4. **a)** $x < 5$ **b)** $x > 1.5$
5. **a)** -2, -1 **b)** -9, -8, -7, -6, -5, -4, -3, -2, -1, 0, 1, 2, 3, 4, 5, 6

Page 47

1. a) **See p.8 for graph** b) i) $y = 0.25$ ii) $x = 1.9$ or $x = -1.9$ (allow ±0.1 for both answers)

2. a)

x	-3	-2	-1	0	1	2
x^2	9	4	1	0	1	4
$+x$	-3	-2	-1	0	1	2
-3	-3	-3	-3	-3	-3	-3
$y = x^2 + x - 3$	3	-1	-3	-3	-1	3

b) **See p.8 for graph**

c) i) $y = 0.75$ ii) $x = 1.7$ or $x = -2.7$

d) $x = 1.3$, $x = -2.3$ e) $x = 1.6$, $x = -2.6$ f) $x = 0.6$, $x = -1.6$

Page 48

3. a)

x	-4	-3	-2	-1	0	1	2
x^2	16	9	4	1	0	1	4
$+2x$	-8	-6	-4	-2	0	+2	+4
-4	-4	-4	-4	-4	-4	-4	-4
$y = x^2 + 2x - 4$	4	-1	-4	-5	-4	-1	4

b) **See p.8 for graph** c) $x = 1.2$, $x = -3.2$

4. -5

5. a)

x	-6	-5	-4	-3	-2	-1	0	1	2
y	6	-1	-6	-9	-10	-9	-6	-1	6

b) **See p.8 for graph** c) $x = 1.2$, $x = -5.2$

6. a) **See p.8 for graph** b) $x = \pm 3.5$

7. a) **See p.8 for graph** b) $x = 3.4$, $x = -2.4$

Page 49

1. a) 1.30pm b) Mr Brown, 2 hours c) Mr Smith, 60mph
   d) They passed each other e) Mr Smith, 30 mins

2. a) 72km/h b) **See p.8 for graph**

3. a) **See p.9 for graph** b) Between 4 and 5 seconds

Page 50

4. a) **See p.9 for graph** b) 2.52pm to 2.58pm

5. a)

miles	0	10	20	30	50	100
cost £	30	33	36	39	45	60

b) **See p.9 for graph** c) £44 to £46

Page 51

6. a) B b) A c) D d) C

7. a)

pounds	10	20	30	40
US dollars	14	28	42	56

b) **See p.9 for graph** c) £21 to £22

8. a) **See p.9 for graph** b) Plumber A c) Plumber B d) After 4 hours

Page 52

1. a) $p = 120°$ (angles on a straight line), $q = 95°$ (angles on a straight line) b) $p = 144°$ (angles on a straight line), $q = 54°$ (vertically opposite angles) c) $p = 55°$ (angles on a straight line), $q = 105°$ (vertically opposite angles) d) $p = 42°$ (angles on a straight line), $q = 48°$ (angles on a straight line) e) $p = 38°$ (vertically opposite angles), $q = 97°$ (angles on a straight line) f) $p = 112°$ (vertically opposite angles), $q = 34°$ (angles on a straight line)

2. a) $c = 40°$ (vertically opposite angles), $d = 40°$ (alternate angles)
   b) $c = 37°$ (vertically opposite angles), $d = 37°$ (corresponding angles)
   c) $c = 134°$ (corresponding angles), $d = 134°$ (vertically opposite angles)

Page 53

3. a) $m = 62°$ (alternate angles), $n = 70°$ (corresponding angles)
   b) $m = 85°$ (allied angles), $n = 70°$ (corresponding angles)
   c) $m = 65°$ (alternate angles), $n = 50°$ (allied angles)

4. $a = 70°$ (allied angles), $b = 70°$ (alternate angles), $c = 110°$ (corresponding angles)

5. $p = 64°$ (corresponding angles), $q = 116°$ (allied angles), $r = 64°$ (alternate angles), $s = 64°$ (corresponding angles)

6. a) $x = 60°$ b) $x = 20°$ c) $x = 36°$ d) $x = 36°$

7. a) $p = 110°$ (alternate angles), $q = 145°$ (allied angles) b) $p = 78°$ (corresponding and alternate angles), $r = 48°$ (angles on a straight line) c) $u = 75°$ (corresponding angles), $v = 75°$ (alternate angles), $w = 75°$ (corresponding angles)

Page 54

1.

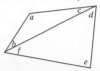

$a = e$ (corresponding), $b = d$ (alternate), $c + d + e = 180°$, $a + b + c = 180°$

2. **Accept same diagram and explanation as for question 1**

3. a) $a = 180° - b$ b) $a = d + f$ c) $a = 360° - (c + e)$ d) $360°$

Page 55

1. a) $x = 70°$ (isosceles) b) $x = 60°$ (scalene) c) $x = 44°$ (right-angled)
   d) $x = 60°$ (equilateral)

2. a) $p = 50°$ b) $p = 40°$ c) $p = 40°$ d) $p = 128°$

3. $a = 65°$ (isosceles triangle), $b = 65°$ (angles on a straight line and angles in triangle)

4. $m = 60°$ (equilateral and vertically opposite), $n = 150°$ (external angles of triangle)

Page 56

1. a) $x = 70°$ (parallelogram) b) $x = 50°$ (kite) c) $x = 75°$ (trapezium)
   d) $x = 110°$ (rhombus)

2. a) Rhombus b) Rectangle c) Square

3. $a + b + c = 180°$, $d + e + f = 180°$, $a + b + c + d + e + f = 360°$

4. a) $p = 56°$ b) $p = 107°$, $q = 95°$ c) $p = 60°$ d) $p = 60°$, $q = 30°$

5. a) $108°$ b) $x = 65°$

Page 57

1. a) $p = 60°$ b) $p = 115°$

2. a) $360°$ b) $360°$

3. a) 4 sides b) $360°$

4. a) 6 sides b) $360°$

5. $74°$

6. a) 6 sides b) 4 sides c) 4 sides

Page 58

7. a) $72°$ b) $108°$

8. a) $60°$ b) $120°$

9. a) $a = 72°$, $b = 54°$ b) $a = 60°$, $b = 60°$

10. No, interior plus exterior equals $180°$

11. a) 5 sides b) $x = 80°$ c) $100°$, $80°$, $20°$, $30°$, $130°$

12. a) $108°$ b) $72°$ c) 5

13. 36 sides

Page 59

1. **See p.9 for diagram**

2. **See p.9 for diagram**

3. a) 4 b) 2 c) 0 d) 2 e) 1 f) 0

4. a) 4 b) 2 c) 1 or none a)–c) **See p.9 for diagrams**

Page 60

5. X: order 2, H: order 2, I: order 2, Z: order 2, K: order 1, S: order 2, E: order 1, N: order 2

6. a) 6 b) 8 c) 5 d) 3

7. a–b) **See p.9 for diagrams** c) 5

8. a) **See p.9 for diagram** b) **See p.9 for diagram**, order 6

9. a) 4 b) 2 c) 2 d) 2 e) 1 or none f) 1 or none

Page 61

1. a) No, given side does not correspond b) Yes, given side and two angles correspond

2. a) i) $x = 6.4$cm ii) $y = 72°$ b) i) $x = 8$cm ii) $y = 80°$

3. **See p.9 for diagram**

4. All three triangles are similar: they have the same angles. The congruent triangles are ABC and PQR, since QR corresponds to AC.

5. Angles in hexagon = $120°$ which will divide into $360°$ (angles at a point). Angles in pentagon = $108°$ which will not divide into $360°$

Page 62

1. a) No, the angles in the triangles are not the same b) Yes, the angles in the triangles are the same

2. a) XY = 10cm b) BC = 3.9cm

3. a) DE = 7.5cm b) BD = 1.5cm

4. ABC and XYZ similar, three corresponding angles

1. **a)** 13cm **b)** 25cm **c)** 7.2cm **d)** 16cm **e)** 10.4cm **f)** 16.4cm
2. Triangle C
3. 9.7cm

Page 64
4. **a)** 6cm **b)** 7.3cm
5. 13.3km
6. **a)** 102.5cm **b)** 11.2cm **c)** 10.0cm
7. Yes, $6.25^2 - 6^2 = 1.75^2$ **or** $6^2 + 1.75^2 = 6.25^2$, etc.
8. 8.5cm
9. 9.5cm
10. **a)** 4.2cm **b)** 3.2cm
11. 11.4cm

Page 65
1. **a)** 23.2cm **b)** 22.1cm **c)** 22.8cm **d)** 33.6 **e)** 16cm **f)** 36cm
2. 600cm
3. 37.2m

Page 66
1. **a)** 14cm² **b)** 13cm²
2. **a)** 36cm² **b)** 10 800cm² **or** 1.08m² **c)** 75cm² **d)** 32cm² **e)** 18cm²
   f) 264cm² **g)** 3550cm²

Page 67
3. **a)** 111.0cm²
4. **a)** 184cm² **b)** 105cm²
5. 29m² area, 4 tins needed at a total cost of £19.96
6. **a) See p.9 for diagram** Area of rectangle = $l \times w = b \times h$ ∴ Area
   of parallelogram = $b \times h$ **b) See p.9 for diagram** Area of
   parallelogram = $b \times h$ ∴ Area of triangle = $\frac{1}{2} b \times h$

Page 68
1. **a)** Centre **b)** Radius **c)** Diameter **d)** Circumference **e)** Chord **f)** Tangent
2. **See p.9 for diagram**
3. **a)** Perimeter of a circle **b)** Distance from centre to circumference
   c) Distance from one side of circle to other through the centre
   d) A straight line joining one side of circle to other <u>not</u> through the
   centre **e)** Touches circumference at 90° to radius. **f)** <u>Part</u> of circumference

Page 69
4. **a)** 6.3cm **b)** 25.1cm **c)** 62.8cm **d)** 30.1cm
5. 6.4m
6. 45.1m
7. **a)** 75.4cm **b)** 7.5cm **c)** 37.7cm **d)** 376.8cm
8. 61.7 cm

Page 70
1. **a)** 616cm² **b)** 1390cm²
2. **a)** 101cm² **b)** 201cm²
3. 941.46cm²

Page 71
1. **a) i)** L **ii)** C **iii)** D **iv)** J **v)** G **vi)** H **b)** Reflection in line $y = 2.5$
   c) Reflection in line $x = 1$
2. **a)** A, Reflection in line $x = -2$; B, Reflection in line $y = x$;
   C, Reflection in line $y = -x$; D, Reflection in line $y = 0.5$

Page 72
3. **a) See p.10 for diagram**
   b) Reflection in the line $y = -0.5$
4. **a)–b) See p.10 for diagrams**
5. **See p.10 for diagram**

Page 73
1. **a) i)** F **ii)** H **iii)** C **b)** $\frac{1}{4}$ turn clockwise about centre (0,0)
2. **See p.10 for diagram**
3. **See p.10 for diagram**

Page 74
1. **a) i)** D **ii)** H **iii)** E **iv)** C **v)** I **vi)** J **b)** $\begin{pmatrix} -4 \\ -2 \end{pmatrix}$ **c)** $\begin{pmatrix} 8 \\ -4 \end{pmatrix}$
2. **See p.10 for diagram**
3. **See p.10 for diagram**

Page 75
1. **See p.10 for grid**
2. **a)** Centre (-1,0), scale factor 2 **b)** Centre (15,1), scale factor $\frac{1}{2}$
3. **See p.11 for grid**

Page 76
1. **a) i)** reflection in line $x = 0$ **ii)** reflection in line $y = 0$ **b)** $\frac{1}{2}$ turn
   around origin (0,0)
2. **a) i)** $\frac{3}{4}$ turn clockwise around origin (0,0) **ii)** reflection in line $y = 0$
   b) reflection in line $y = x$
3. **a)–b) See p.11 for grid c)** $\frac{1}{2}$ turn around centre (1,1)
4. **a)–d) See p.11 for grid e)** $\frac{1}{2}$ turn around centre (2,0)
   f) reflection in line $x = y$

Page 77
1–2. **See p.11 for diagram**
3. **a)–b) See p.11 for diagram**

Page 78
4. **See p.11 for diagram**
5. **See p.11 for diagram**

Page 79
6. **a)–c) See p.11 for diagram**
7. **a) See p.11 for diagram b)** All angle bisectors intersect in the
   middle of the triangle
8. **Accept correctly constructed triangle and square**
9. **a)–d) Accept correctly constructed triangles**

Page 80
1. **See p.11 for diagram**
2. **See p.11 for diagram**
3. **a)–c) See p.11 for diagram**
4. **a)–b) See p.11 for diagram**

Page 81
1. **a)** Rectangle **b)** AB, EF, GH **c)** DE, CF, BG **d)** 8
2. **a)** 12 **b)** 7 **c)** 7
3. **a)–b) See p.11 for diagrams**
4. $F = 5$, $E = 8$, $V = 5$ ∴ $5 + 5 - 8 = 2$

Page 82
1. **a)–c) See p.11 for diagrams**
2. **a)** Parallelogram prism **b)** 8 **c) See p.12 for diagram**
3. **a)** and **d)** are correct nets
4. All sides 3cm. Hexagons can be anywhere as long as one on top and
   one on bottom. **See p.12 for diagram**
5. **a)–c) See p.12 for diagrams**

Page 83
1. **a)** 160cm³ **b)** 216cm³ **c)** 30cm³
2. **a)** 81cm³ **b)** 785cm³ **c)** 942cm³
3. **a)** 5cm **b)** 5cm **c)** 6.25cm

Page 84
4. **a)** 25cm **b)** 2cm
5. 39.5cm
6. 1656m³
7. **a)** 628cm³ **b)** 6.4cm

Page 85
1. **a) See p.12 for diagram**, all measurements in cm **b)** 29.25m
2. **a)** 61km **b)** 24km **c)** Bodmin, Fowey and Holsworthy
3. **a) See p.12 for diagram**, Scale 1cm = 10m **b)** 94m
4. **a) See p.12 for diagram b)** 6.3m

Page 86
1. **a)** 28cm **b)** 72cm²
2. 540cm³
3. **a)** 100cm² **b)** 432cm³

Page 87
1. **a)** 4.5m **b)** 3500ml **c)** 1250g **d)** 6.874kg **e)** 45 000m **f)** 5.5mm
2. **a)** 10.05m **b)** 1937m **c)** 2.65m
3. 4220mg, 0.405kg, 420g, 4kg, 39.5kg
4. **a)** 18 inches **b)** 180g **c)** 22.5 litres
5. Jake by 20cm
6. 1200m, 1 050 000mm, 1km, 900m, 11 000cm
7. **a)** 4.8km **b)** 7.5 miles **c)** 2025g **d)** 0.8 pounds **e)** 6.9 litres **f)** 39.4 pints
8. 11 000 yards

Page 88
1. **a) i)** 090° **ii)** 048° **iii)** 125° **iv)** 225° **v)** 270° **vi)** 305°
   b) i) 30km **ii)** 50km **iii)** 30km

2. A → B: 045°
B → C: 145°
C → D: 215°
D → A: 308°

3. a) See p.12 for diagram **b)** 313°
4. See p.12 for diagram

Page 89
1. 1h 40min
2. 11.2mph
3. 24m
4. 92.5km/h
5. a) 108km/h **b)** 378km

Page 90
1. 12.3 cm
2. 10.7 cm
3. $x = 48°$, $y = 151°$
4. 11.2 cm (allow ± 0.1 cm)

Page 91
1. a) i) $\frac{4}{10} = \frac{2}{5}$ **ii)** $\frac{3}{10}$ **iii)** $\frac{2}{10} = \frac{1}{5}$ **iv)** $\frac{1}{10}$ **v)** $\frac{6}{10} = \frac{3}{5}$ **vi)** $\frac{7}{10}$

b) i–iv)

```
   0           0.5          1
   |------------|------------|
      D C B A
```

2. a) $\frac{4}{18} = \frac{2}{9}$ **b)** $\frac{14}{18} = \frac{7}{9}$ **c)** $\frac{5}{18}$ **d)** $\frac{13}{18}$ **e)** $\frac{9}{18} = \frac{1}{2}$ **f)** $\frac{9}{18} = \frac{1}{2}$

3. a) $\frac{1}{2}$ **b)** $\frac{1}{2}$ **c)** $\frac{10}{30} = \frac{1}{3}$ **d)** $\frac{22}{30} = \frac{11}{15}$ **e)** $\frac{8}{30} = \frac{4}{15}$

4. a) $\frac{2}{5}$ **b)** $\frac{3}{5}$ **c)** 0

Page 92
5. a) (2 of spades, 2 of diamonds) (2 of spades, 2 of hearts) (5 of spades, 2 of diamonds) (5 of spades, 2 of hearts) **b) i)** $\frac{2}{6} = \frac{1}{3}$ **ii)** $\frac{1}{6}$ **iii)** $\frac{5}{6}$
6. 0.3
7. 0.35
8. a) $\frac{1}{8}$ **b)** $\frac{1}{2}$
9. a) $\frac{7}{10}$ **b)** $\frac{3}{10}$ **c)** $\frac{3}{10}$ **d)** $\frac{7}{10}$ **e)** 1 **f)** 0
10. a) i) $\frac{3}{12} = \frac{1}{4}$ **ii)** $\frac{6}{12} = \frac{1}{2}$ **iii)** $\frac{2}{12} = \frac{1}{6}$ **b) i)** $\frac{3}{4}$ **ii)** $\frac{1}{2}$ **iii)** $\frac{5}{6}$ **c)** 24

Page 93
1. a)

		First Die					
		1	2	3	4	5	6
Second Die	1	2	3	4	5	6	7
	2	3	4	5	6	7	8
	3	4	5	6	7	8	9
	4	5	6	7	8	9	10
	5	6	7	8	9	10	11
	6	7	8	9	10	11	12

b) i) $\frac{6}{36} = \frac{1}{6}$ **ii)** $\frac{15}{36} = \frac{5}{12}$ **iii)** $\frac{15}{36} = \frac{5}{12}$ **iv)** $\frac{7}{36}$ **v)** 0 **vi)** $\frac{12}{36} = \frac{1}{3}$ **vii)** $\frac{12}{36} = \frac{1}{3}$

2. a)

		Francis's Coin					
		1p	1p	2p	10p	20p	20p
Jim's Coin	1p	2p	2p	3p	11p	21p	21p
	2p	3p	3p	4p	12p	22p	22p
	5p	6p	6p	7p	15p	25p	25p
	5p	6p	6p	7p	15p	25p	25p
	10p	11p	11p	12p	20p	30p	30p
	50p	51p	51p	52p	60p	70p	70p

b) i) $\frac{4}{36} = \frac{1}{9}$ **ii)** $\frac{3}{36} = \frac{1}{12}$ **iii)** $\frac{12}{36} = \frac{1}{3}$ **iv)** $\frac{6}{36} = \frac{1}{6}$ **v)** $\frac{5}{6}$ **vi)** 0

3. a)

		Bruce's Die					
		1	2	3	4	5	6
Robin's Spinner	2	2	4	6	8	10	12
	4	4	8	12	16	20	24
	8	8	16	24	32	40	48
	9	9	18	27	36	45	54
	10	10	20	30	40	50	60

b) i) $\frac{2}{30} = \frac{1}{15}$ **ii)** $\frac{2}{30} = \frac{1}{15}$ **iii)** $\frac{9}{30} = \frac{3}{10}$ **iv)** $\frac{19}{30}$ **v)** $\frac{3}{30} = \frac{1}{10}$

vi) $\frac{27}{30} = \frac{9}{10}$

Page 94
1. a) i) 60 **ii)** 40 **iii)** 20 **b)** 1 – 0.55, 2 – 0.32, 3 – 0.13
2. a) 0.44, 0.53, 0.46, 0.48 **b)** See p.12 for graph
   c) 0.5, theoretically $\frac{1}{2}$ landing on tails
3. a) 0.1, 0.08, 0.11, 0.13, 0.15, 0.16, 0.17, 0.18, 0.17, 0.16, 0.16, 0.16
   b) See p.12 for graph **c)** 250

Page 95
1. a) Interpret and discuss the data.
   b) Process and represent the data.
2. a) Some examples are…
   Taking observations e.g. Number of occupants in cars
   Results from an experiment
   A survey
   Records of historical data e.g weather conditions.
   Or any other sensible answer
3. A sensible answer will include:
   a) Specify the problem and plan:
   Give your interpretation of the problem and define more precisely what you are trying to find out.
   Develop some outline ideas on how the data will be collected and how it might be used to provide the answers you are looking for.
   b) Decide what data to collect
   Consider the various forms of exercise that pupils may take. Allow for others.
   Develop a data collection sheet that will provide the information that you need.
   c) Collect.data from a variety of sources
   Consider different primary sources. Decide whether Secondary data may be used?
   d) Process and represent the data
   Consider what calculations may be used with the data and how your results may be presented.
   e) Interpret and discuss the data
   Decide what your results mean and try to come to some conclusions relating to your original interpretation of the problem.
   Consider further lines of inquiry.
4. Some suggestions for using the data handling cycle are to:
   • Compare the performance of boys and girls in mathematics.
   • Compare the height/weight of modern teenagers with those from, say, 50 years ago.
   • Determine the influence that watching television has on performance in school.
   • Consider the effectiveness of different training methods used for top athletes.
   • Compare the music that young people like to listen to in different countries.
   • You could use the data handling cycle to try and answer questions such as:
     • How much exercise do you need to stay healthy?
     • Does brain training make any difference?
     • In which sport do the competitors make most money?

Page 96
1. Primary data is obtained <u>first</u> hand usually by yourself. Secondary data is obtained from an external agency, e.g. data from internet.
2. a) Choosing a reliable, balanced group of people, ages, sex, etc.
   b) No, should be taken from all over UK, males and females.
3. a) Not suitable – leading question **b)** Suitable – establishes if eat breakfast **c)** Suitable – may not have time for breakfast **d)** Not suitable – not relevant **e)** Suitable – establishes age group **f)** Suitable but vague – establishes what they eat **g)** Suitable – differences **h)** Not suitable – not relevant

Page 97
4. a) Accept any suitable questions b) Accept any suitable questions, e.g. Do you agree we are the best supermarket?
5. a) Accept any suitable observation sheet design
   b) Accept any suitable answer, e.g. conducting the survey in different schools across all year groups
6. a) Accept any suitable answers b) Accept any suitable answers

7. **a)** Accept any suitable observation sheet design **b)** Accept any suitable answer, e.g. by asking girls and boys from all year groups in the playground.

Page 98
1. Discrete data can only take certain values. Continuous data can take any value (within a range) and is often collected by measurement.
2. **Frequency:** 4, 7, 8, 12, 9, **Total:** 40
3. **a) Frequency:** 3, 5, 8, 13, 9, 2, **Total:** 40 **b)** 80%

Page 99
4. **Frequency:** 2, 3, 5, 9, 1, **Total:** 20
5. **a) Frequency:** 3, 12, 12, 3, **Total:** 30 **b)** 50%
6. **Frequency:** 11, 19, 5, 0, 3, **Total:** 38
7. **a) Frequency:** 1, 4, 8, 8, 4, 3, 2, **Total:** 30 **b)** $83\frac{1}{3}$%
8. **Frequency:** 2, 1, 7, 3, 7, 8, 8, 3, 1, **Total:** 40

Page 100
1.
```
0 | 8 9
1 | 0 7
2 | 1 3 8 9
3 | 0 1 4 4 8
4 | 1 1 2 4 5 6 7 7
5 | 1 2 5 6 7 8
6 | 0 8
7 | 4
```
Key: 4|1 = 41 years

2.

	Men	Women	Children
Listen to Radio	32	41	73
Do Not Listen to Radio	23	24	47
TOTAL	55	65	120

3. **a)**

	Year 7	Year 8	Year 9	TOTAL
Pop	42	30	18	90
Rap	16	12	13	41
Dance	14	24	31	69
TOTAL	72	66	62	200

   b) 45%

4. **a)**
```
16 | 4 6 7 9 9
17 | 0 1 1 3 3 3 4 4 5 5 6 8 8 8 8 9
18 | 0 1 2 4 6 8 9
19 | 1 2
```
Key: 6|4 =164cm

   b) $170 \leqslant h < 180$ **c)** $175\frac{1}{2}$cm

Page 101
1. **See p.12 for diagram**
2. **See p.12 for diagram**
3. **a)** 2010
   b) A higher proportion of semi-skimmed milk was sold in 2010.
   c) Semi-skimmed milk has been promoted as the healthier option in the years between 2000 and 2010.

Page 102
1. **See p.12 for diagram**
2. **a) See p.13 for diagram**
   b) See p.13 for diagram
   c) Women generally spend more on cosmetics than men: modal amount women $4 \leqslant M < 6$, modal amount men $2 \leqslant M < 4$
3. **a)**

Temperature (°C)	Frequency
$15 \leqslant T < 20$	11
$20 \leqslant T < 25$	13
$25 \leqslant T < 30$	9
$30 \leqslant T < 35$	7
TOTAL	40

   b) See p.13 for diagram
   c) See p.13 for diagram

Page 103
1. **a)** The longer the journey time the greater the distance travelled (positive correlation)
   b) See p.13 for diagram
   c) i) 42.5 minutes **ii)** 1.6km
2. **a) See p.13 for diagram**
   b) Positive correlation – as height increases weight increases
   c) i) Accept answers around 139cm ii) Accept answers around 86kg

Page 104
3. **a) See p.13 for diagram**
   b) Negative, as change received increases number of items decreases.
   c) i) £4.40 **ii)** 6 items
4. **a) See p.13 for diagram**
   b) i) 61 mins **ii)** 8 tracks
5. **a) See p.13 for diagram**
   b) The more chapters the more pages – positive
   c) i) 300 pages **ii)** 15 chapters

Page 105
1. **a) See p.13 for diagram**
   b) 35% **c)** $\frac{1}{10}$
2. **a) i)** 24 **ii)** 20 **b)** Women: 12 men, 15 women
3. **a) See p.13 for diagram**
   b) 40%
4. **a)** 1–20: 18, 21–40: 8, 41–60: 6, 61–80: 6, 81–100: 2, Total: 40
   b) See p.13 for diagram
   c) 35%
5. **a) i)** 6 **ii)** 8 **b) i)** 24 **ii)** 36

Page 106
1. **Mean:** 6p, **Median:** 2p, **Mode:** 2p, **Range:** 19p
2. **Mean:** £205, **Median:** £210.50, **Mode:** £248, **Range:** £95
3. **a) Mean:** 56kg, **Median:** 53, **Mode:** 51, **Range:** 19
   b) Average weight, lower with smaller distribution of weights
4. **a) Mean:** 1.56m, **Median:** 1.59m, **Mode:** 1.62m, **Range:** 0.32m
   b) Same range of heights but boys' average height is 12cm bigger

Page 107
1. **a)** 40 **b)** 1 **c)** 1 **d)** 4 **e)** 1.5
2. **a)** 24 **b)** 4 **c)** 3 **d)** 3
3. **a)** £4.13 **b)** $2 \leqslant M < 4$ **c)** $2 \leqslant M < 4$
4. **a)** $\frac{563}{38}$ = 17.06 seconds **b)** $16 < t \leqslant 18$ **c)** $16 < t \leqslant 18$

Page 108
1. $\frac{2}{5}$ of 60miles = 24 miles.

   Time taken to travel 24 miles at 30 mph = 48 minutes.
   Remaining distance = 36 miles.
   Time taken to travel 36 miles at 40 mph = 54 minutes.
   Total travel time = 102 minutes = 1 hour 42 minutes.
   Latest time Josh can leave is 1.18 pm

Page 109
2. **a)** For 100 miles, Deal 1 costs £25 + £10 = £35
   Deal 2 costs £55
   In this case, **Deal 1 is better.**
   b) For 350 miles, Deal 1 costs £25 + £35 = £60
   Deal 2 costs £55
   In this case, **Deal 2 is better.**
   c) For 600 miles, Deal 1 costs £25 + £60 = £85
   Deal 2 costs £55 + £40 = £95
   In this case, **Deal 1 is better.**

Page 110
3. **a)** £4.50 + £6 = £10.50
   b) Two 4-seaters: 2 × £10.50 = £21
   One 6-seater: £6.50 + £9 = £15.50
   The minimum cost is £15.50
   c) £8 + £12 = £20

Page 111
4. £250 000 × 1.12 × 1.11 × 0.85 = £264 180

Answers to Graphs and Diagrams

Page 42, 1.

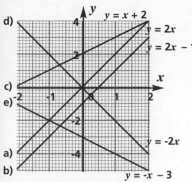

d) $y = x + 2$
$y = 2x$
$y = 2x - 1$
c)
e)
a)
b) $y = -x - 3$
$y = -2x$

Page 42, 2. b)

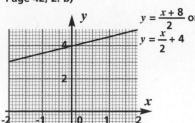

$y = \dfrac{x + 8}{2}$ or
$y = \dfrac{x}{2} + 4$

Page 42, 3. b)

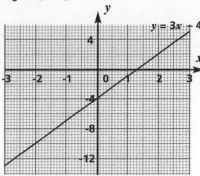

$y = 3x - 4$

Page 42, 4. a)

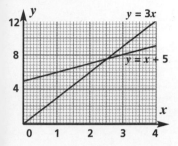

$y = 3x$
$y = x + 5$

Page 47, 1. a)

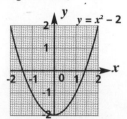

$y = x^2 - 2$

Page 47, 2. b)

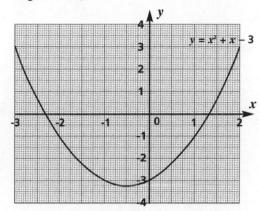

$y = x^2 + x - 3$

Page 48, 3. b)

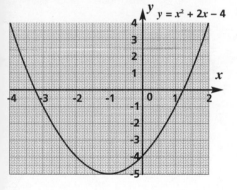

$y = x^2 + 2x - 4$

Page 48, 5. b)

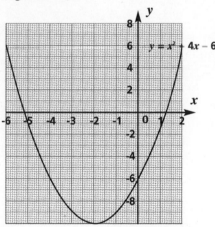

$y = x^2 + 4x - 6$

Page 48, 6. a)

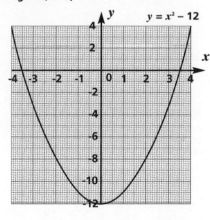

$y = x^2 - 12$

Page 48, 7. a)

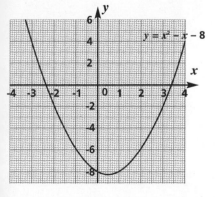

$y = x^2 - x - 8$

Page 49, 2. b)

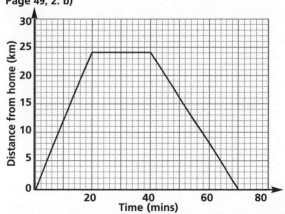

Page 49, 3. a)

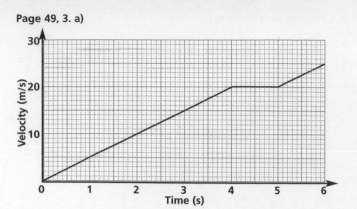

Page 50, 4. a)

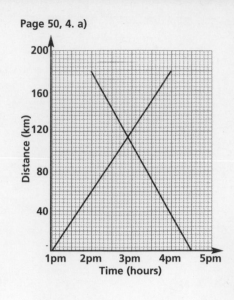

Page 50, 5. b)

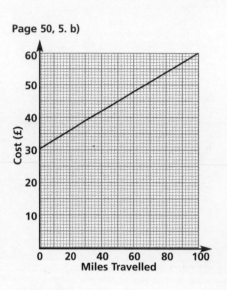

Page 51, 7. b)

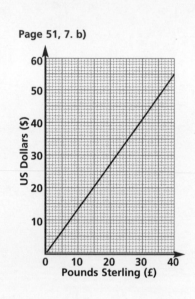

Page 51, 8. a)

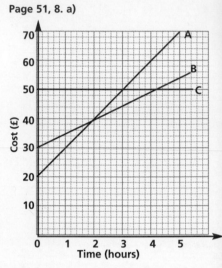

Page 59, 1.

Page 59, 2.

M S H B Z A V C K

Page 59, 4.

a)   b)   c)

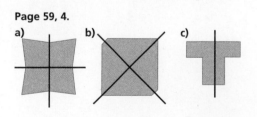

Page 60, 7. a)

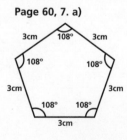

Page 60, 7. b)

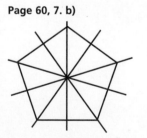

Page 60, 8. a)

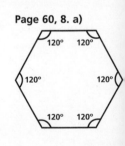

Page 60, 8. b)

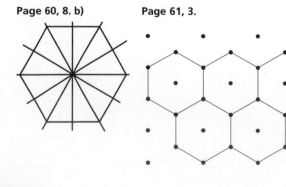

Page 61, 3.

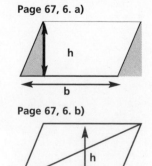

Page 67, 6. a)

Page 67, 6. b)

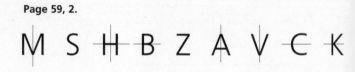

Page 68, 2.

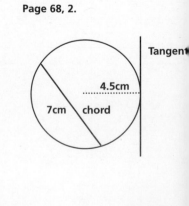

Page 72, 3. a)

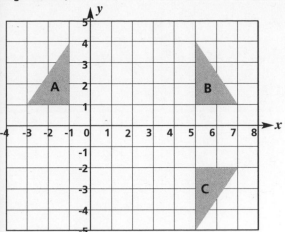

Page 72, 4. a)–b)

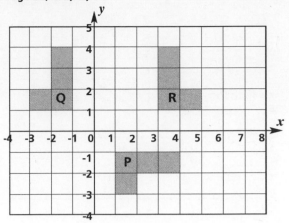

Page 72, 5.

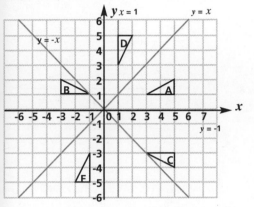

Page 73, 2.

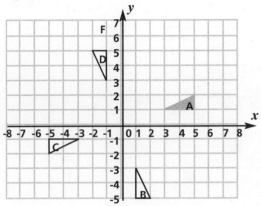

Page 73, 3.

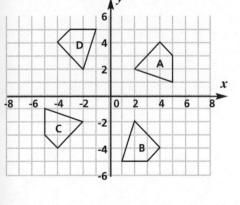

Page 74, 2.

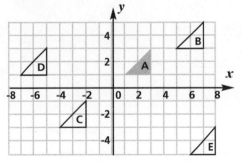

Page 74, 3.

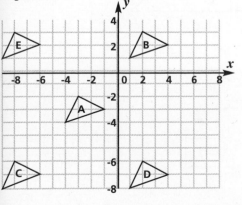

Page 75, 1.

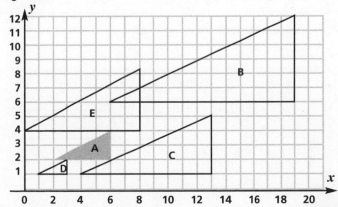

Page 75, 3.

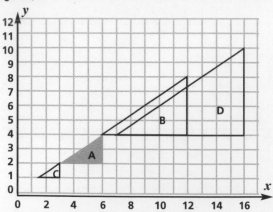

Page 76, 3. a–b)

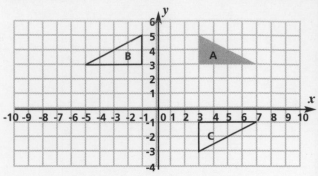

Page 76, 4. a–d)

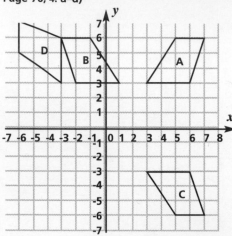

Page 77, 1–2.

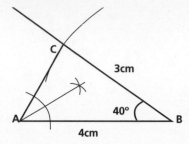

Page 77, 3.

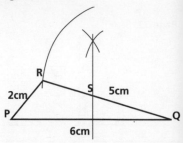

Page 78, 4.

Scale: 1cm = 10km

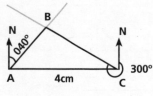

Page 78, 5.

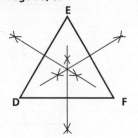

Page 79, 6. a)–c)

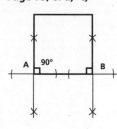

Page 79, 7. a)

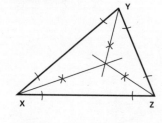

Page 80, 1.

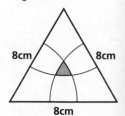

Page 80, 2.

1cm = 2m

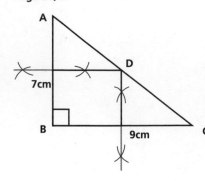

Page 80, 3.

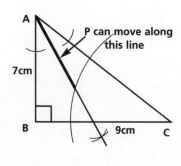

Page 80, 4.

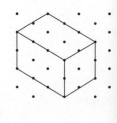

Page 81, 3. a)

Page 81, 3. b)

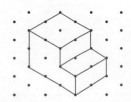

Page 82, 1. a)

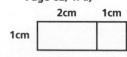

Page 82, 1. b)

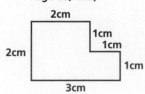

Page 82, 1. c)

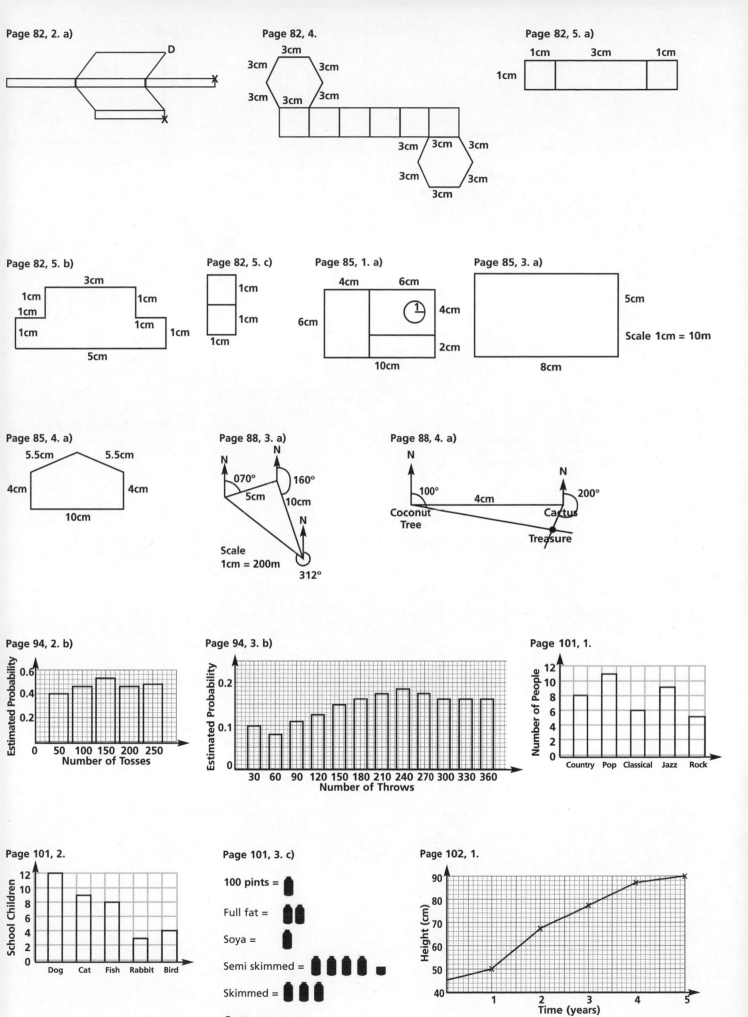

Page 82, 2. a)

Page 82, 4.

Page 82, 5. a)

Page 82, 5. b)

Page 82, 5. c)

Page 85, 1. a)

Page 85, 3. a)

Page 85, 4. a)

Page 88, 3. a)

Page 88, 4. a)

Page 94, 2. b)

Page 94, 3. b)

Page 101, 1.

Page 101, 2.

Page 101, 3. c)

Page 102, 1.

Page 102, 2.

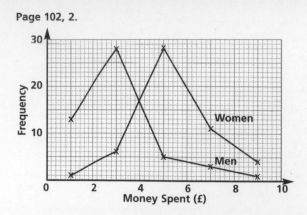

Page 102, 3. b)

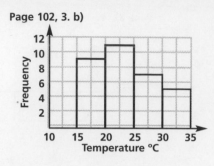

Page 102, 3. c)

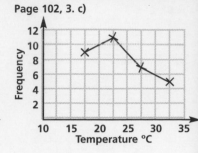

Page 103, 1. b)

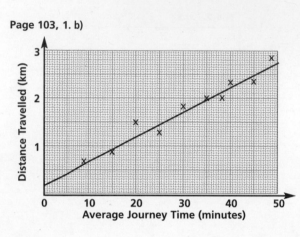

Page 103, 2. a)

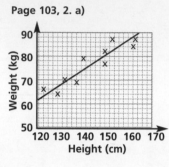

Page 104, 3. a)

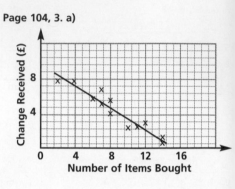

Page 104, 4. a)

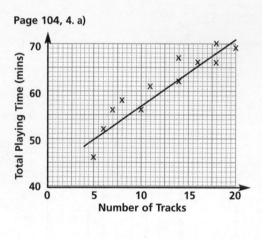

Page 104, 5. a)

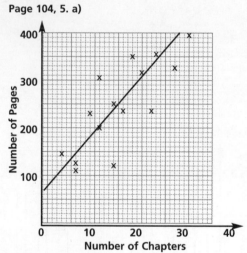

Page 105, 1. a)

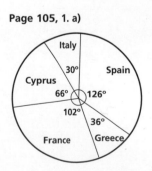

Page 105, 3. a)

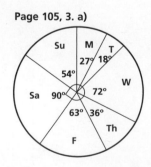

Page 105, 4. b)

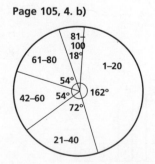

Published by Lonsdale

© 2010 Lonsdale

Irregular Polygons

1 For each diagram below work out the size of angle *p*. They are not drawn to scale.

a)

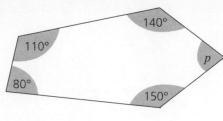

b)

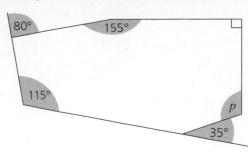

....

....

....

2 **a)** What do the exterior angles of an irregular pentagon add up to? ....

b) What do the exterior angles of a regular pentagon add up to? ....

3 **An irregular polygon has exterior angles equal to 110°, 94°, 88° and 68°.**

a) How many sides does the polygon have? ....

b) What is the sum of the interior angles of this irregular polygon?

....

....

4 **An irregular polygon has interior angles equal to 110°, 155°, 135°, 95°, 140° and 85°.**

a) How many sides does the polygon have? ....

b) What is the sum of the exterior angles of this irregular polygon?

....

....

5 **An irregular pentagon has four exterior angles equal to 47°, 113°, 55° and 71°. What is the size of the fifth exterior angle?**

....

6 **a)** How many sides does a polygon have if the sum of its interior angles is twice the sum of its exterior angles? ....

b) How many sides does a regular polygon have if each interior angle is equal to each exterior angle?

....

c) How many sides does a polygon have if the sum of its interior angles is equal to the sum of its exterior angles? ....

Regular Polygons

7 **A regular polygon has five sides.**

Calculate the size of **a)** each exterior angle and

b) each interior angle.

....

....

....

....

....

....

8 **A regular polygon has six sides.**

Calculate the size of **a)** each exterior angle and

b) each interior angle.

....

....

....

....

....

....

9 **The diagrams below show regular polygons, centre 0. For each polygon work out the size of the angles marked a and b.**

a)

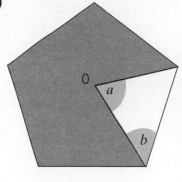

b)

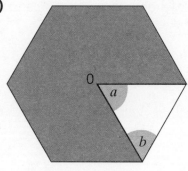

....

....

....

....

....

....

....

....

10 **Jon reckons that it is possible to have a regular polygon where each interior angle is equal to 150° and each exterior angle is equal to 40°. Is he correct? Explain.**

....

....

11 **A polygon has interior angles equal to $x°$, $x + 20°$, $2x°$, $2x - 10°$ and 50°.**
   a) How many sides does this polygon have?
   b) Work out the size of x.
   c) What is the size of each exterior angle?

12 **A regular polygon has each interior angle equal to $1\frac{1}{2}$ times each exterior angle.**
   a) What is the size of each interior angle?
   b) What is the size of each exterior angle?
   c) How many sides does this regular polygon have?

13 **A regular polygon has each interior angle equal to 170°. How many sides does it have?**

Symmetry

1 Draw all the lines of symmetry for each of the following shapes:

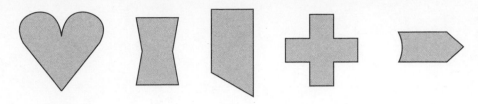

2 Mark on the lines of symmetry for each of these letters:

M S H B Z A V C K

3 How many lines of symmetry do each of the following quadrilaterals have?

a) Square ☐ ....

b) Rectangle ▭ ....

c) Parallelogram ▱ ....

d) Rhombus ◇ ....

e) Kite ◁▷ ....

f) Trapezium ◺ ....

4 For each of the following shapes draw all the lines of symmetry and write down the order of rotational symmetry.

a)

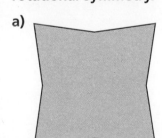

Order of rotational symmetry:

....

b)

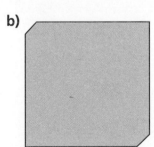

Order of rotational symmetry:

....

c)

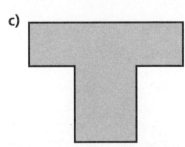

Order of rotational symmetry:

....

Symmetry

5 **What is the order of rotational symmetry for each of these letters?**

X   H   I   Z   K   S   E   N

....

6 **What is the order of rotational symmetry for each of these shapes?**

a)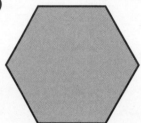

b)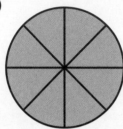

c)

d)

Order: ....   Order: ....   Order: ....   Order: ....

7 **a)** Draw accurately a regular pentagon with sides 3cm long and internal angles 108°.

b) Mark on the lines of symmetry.

c) What is the order of rotational symmetry?...

8 **a)** Draw a regular hexagon. Interior angles are 120°.
   b) Draw in all lines of symmetry and write down the order of rotational symmetry.

9 **Write down the order of rotational symmetry for each quadrilateral:**
   a) Square   **b)** Rectangle   **c)** Parallelogram   **d)** Rhombus   **e)** Kite   **f)** Trapezium.

Congruence and Tessellation

1 Here are four triangles (not drawn to scale).

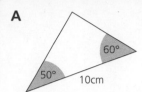 A

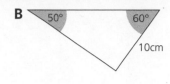 B

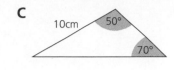 C

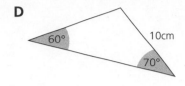 D

a) Peter thinks that triangles B and D are congruent. Is he correct? Explain.

....

....

b) Petra thinks that triangles A and C are congruent. Is she correct? Explain.

....

....

2 a) These two triangles are congruent.

They are not drawn to scale.

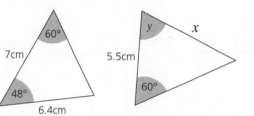

b) These two quadrilaterals are congruent.

They are not drawn to scale.

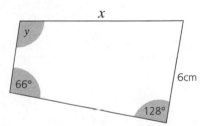

i) What is x? ....

ii) What is y? ....

i) What is x? ....

ii) What is y? ....

3 On the isometric grid below tessellate regular hexagons of side unit 1.

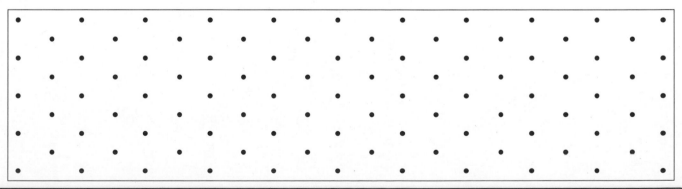

4 Here are three triangles (not drawn to scale).
Which two triangles are congruent? Explain

5 A regular hexagon will form a tessellation
pattern but a regular pentagon does not.
Explain why.

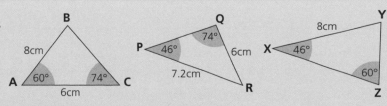

Similarity

1 **Here are four triangles (not drawn to scale).**

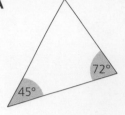 A

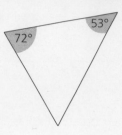 B

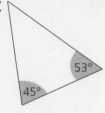 C

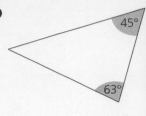 D

a) Pam thinks that triangles B and C are similar. Is she correct? Explain.

....

....

b) Ian thinks that triangles A and D are similar. Is he correct? Explain.

....

....

2 **These two triangles are similar. Calculate the length of...**

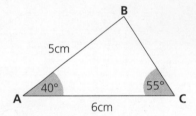

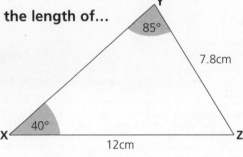

a) XY ....

b) BC ....

3 **In the diagram below BC is parallel to DE. AB = 3 cm, AC = 4cm, BC = 5cm and CE = 2cm.**

The diagram is not drawn to scale.

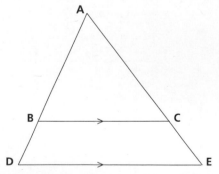

a) Calculate the length of DE.

....

....

....

b) Calculate the length of BD.

....

....

....

4 **Here are three triangles (not drawn to scale).**
Which two triangles are similar? Explain.

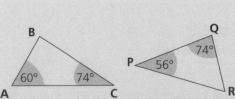

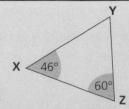

Pythagoras' Theorem

1. Use Pythagoras' theorem to calculate the unknown side in each of the following triangles (not drawn to scale). Where appropriate, give your answer to 1 decimal place.

a)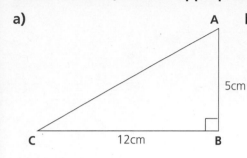

....
....
....

b)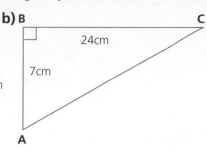

....
....
....

c)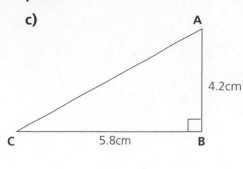

....
....
....

d)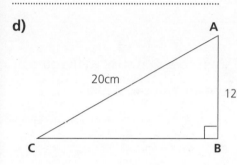

....
....
....

e)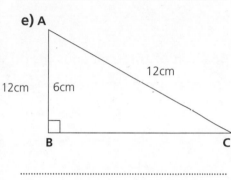

....
....
....

f)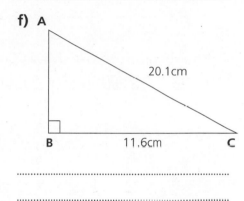

....
....
....

2. Which of the following triangles is not a right-angled triangle? Show all your working. They are not drawn to scale.

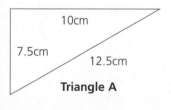

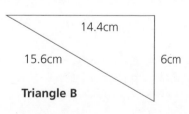

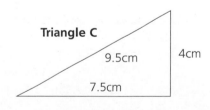

....
....
....

3. Calculate the height of the isosceles triangle alongside, whose sides measure 10cm, 10cm and 5cm. Give your answer to 2 significant figures. The triangle is not drawn to scale.

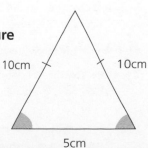

....
....

Pythagoras' Theorem

4 Look at the diagram below (not drawn to scale). Use Pythagoras' theorem to calculate...

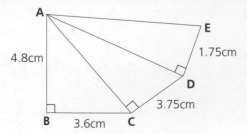

a) the length of AC. ....

....

....

....

b) the length of AE to 1 decimal place.

....

....

....

....

5 The diagram below shows the position of three villages (not drawn to scale). Use Pythagoras' theorem to calculate the direct distance from Lampton to Campton to 1 decimal place.

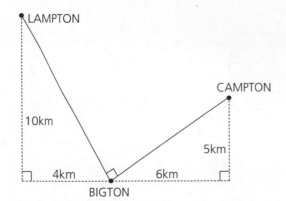

....

....

....

....

....

....

....

....

6 The diagram opposite shows a right-angled triangle ABC.
Use Pythagoras' Theorem to calculate...
a) the length of AB to 1 decimal place if BC = 80cm and AC = 1.3m.
b) the length of AC to 1 decimal place if AB = 10cm and the area of triangle ABC is 25cm².
c) the length of AB to 1 decimal place if AB = BC and AC = 14.2cm.

7 Triangle ABC has AB = 1.75cm, BC = 6cm and AC = 6.25cm. Is triangle ABC a right-angled triangle?
Explain your answer.

8 A square has an area of 36cm². Calculate the length of its diagonal to 1 decimal place.

9 A rectangle has an area of 36cm² and the length of its base is twice that of its height.
Calculate the length of its diagonal.

10 A 4.5m ladder leans against a wall. The foot of the ladder is 1.5m from the base of the wall.
a) How high up the wall does the ladder reach? Give your answer to 1 decimal place.
b) The position of the ladder is now changed so that the distance from the foot of the ladder to the base of the wall is the same as the distance the ladder reaches up the wall. How high up the wall does the ladder now reach, to 1 decimal place?

11 The length of the diagonal of a rectangle is 12cm. The length of its base is three times that of its height.
Calculate the length of the base.

Perimeter

1 Calculate the perimeter of the following shapes. Where lengths are not given, use a ruler to measure the sides.

a)

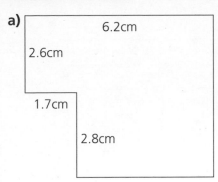

6.2cm
2.6cm
1.7cm
2.8cm

....

....

b)

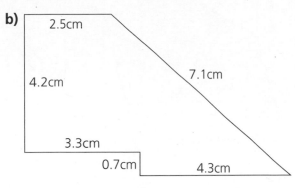

2.5cm
4.2cm
7.1cm
3.3cm
0.7cm
4.3cm

....

....

c)

....

....

d)

....

....

e)

....

....

f)

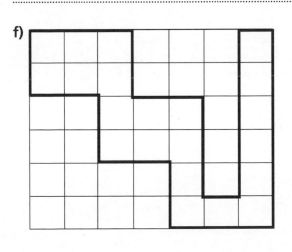

....

....

2 A window measures 200cm by 100cm. Calculate the perimeter of the window.

3 A wall measures 3.6m by 15m. Calculate the perimeter of the wall.

Area

1 Estimate the area for the following shapes. Each square has an area of 1cm².

a)
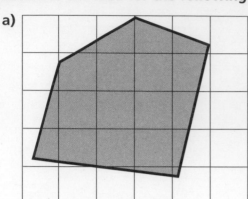

b)
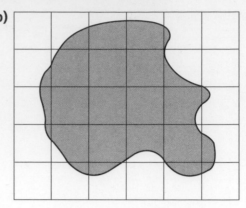

....

2 Calculate the area of the following shapes. They are not drawn to scale.

a)
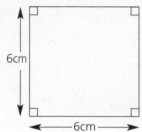
6cm
6cm

b)
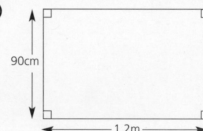
90cm
1.2m

c)
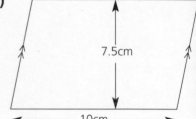
7.5cm
10cm

....

....

d)
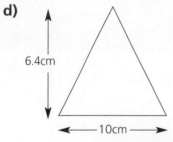
6.4cm
10cm

e)
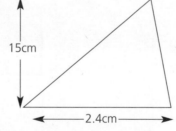
15cm
2.4cm

f)
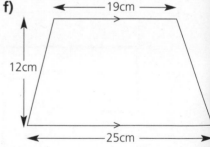
19cm
12cm
25cm

....

....

g)
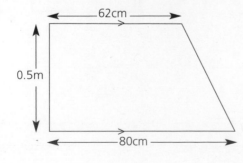
62cm
0.5m
80cm

....

....

3 Calculate the area of the following shape to 1 d.p. (not drawn to scale).

a)

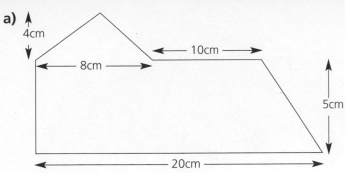

....

....

....

....

....

4 Calculate the surface area of the following solids (not drawn to scale) to 1 d.p. where necessary.

a)

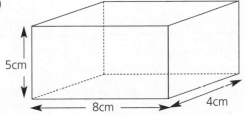

b)

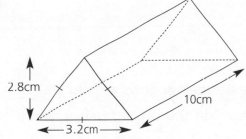

....

....

....

....

5 A property developer decides to varnish the floorboards in the living room of one of his houses. A plan of the floor is shown alongside (not to scale). One tin of varnish will cover 16m² and costs £4.99. If he wants to apply two coats of varnish to the whole floor, how much will it cost him?

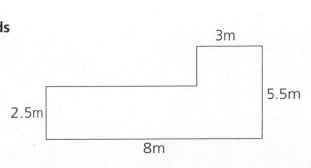

6 Deduce the formula for the area of **a)** a parallelogram   **b)** a triangle.

Circles

1 **Name each of the parts of the circle labelled A to F.**

a) A ....

b) B ....

c) C ....

d) D ....

e) E ....

f) F ....

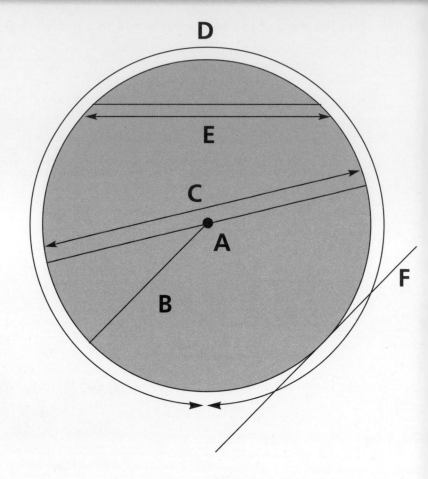

2 **In the space below draw a circle with a radius of 4.5cm. Draw a tangent at the point where the radius touches the circumference, and then draw a chord which measures 7cm.**

3 **Write a brief definition for the following:** a) Circumference b) Radius c) Diameter d) Chord e) Tangent f) Arc

Circles

4 Calculate the circumference of the following circles to 1 decimal place. Take π = 3.14

a)
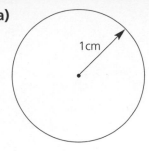

1cm

b)
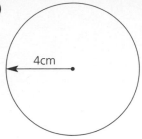

4cm

c)
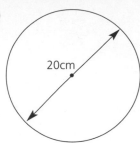

20cm

d)
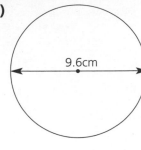

9.6cm

....
....
....
....

5 A window is in the shape of a semi-circle on top of a rectangle as shown in the diagram.

If AB = 1.8m and BC = 90cm, calculate the perimeter of the window to 1 decimal place.

Take π = 3.14

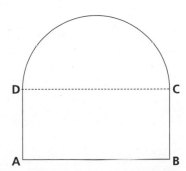

....
....
....
....
....
....

6 Mrs Jones' garden is rectangular. At each end there is a semi-circular flower bed and the rest

of the garden is lawn, as shown in the diagram. If AB = 10m and BC = 8m, calculate the

perimeter of the lawn. Take π = 3.14

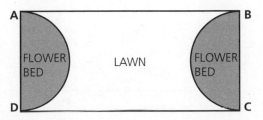

....
....
....
....
....

7 Calculate the circumference of the following circles to 1 decimal place. Take π = 3.14

a) Radius = 12cm   b) Radius = 1.2cm   c) Diameter = 12cm   d) Diameter = 120cm

8 Calculate the perimeter of a semi-circle with diameter 24cm. Give your answer correct to 3 sig. fig.

Circles and Compound Area

1 Calculate the areas of these circles. Give your answers correct to 3 sig. fig.

a)

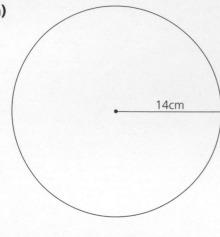

14cm

b)

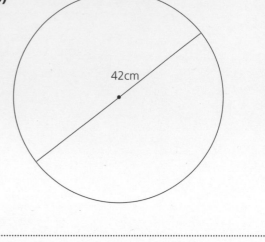

42cm

....

....

....

....

2 Calculate the areas of these shapes. Give your answers correct to 3 sig. fig.

a)

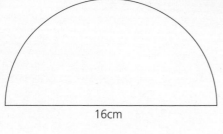

16cm

b)

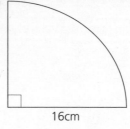

16cm

....

....

....

....

3 Find the area of this shape. Give your answer correct to
2 d.p.

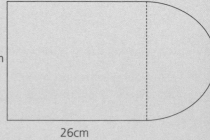

26cm

26cm

Transformations

1 **The grid shows twelve shapes A to L.**

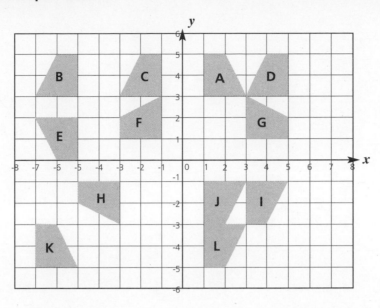

a) Which image is object A reflected…

   i) in the *x*-axis .... **ii)** in the *y*-axis .... **iii)** in the line *x* = 3 ....

   iv) in the line *y* = 1 .... **v)** in the line *y* = *x* .... **vi)** in the line *y* = -*x* ....

b) Describe the single transformation which takes B to E. ....

c) Describe the single transformation which takes F to G. ....

2 **Triangles A, B, C and D are all reflections of the black triangle. For each one draw in the mirror line and describe the reflection fully.**

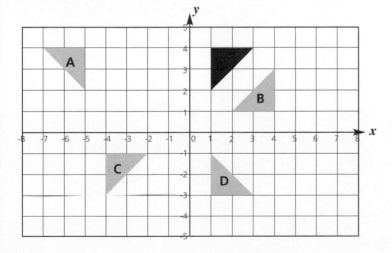

Triangle A: ....

....

Triangle B: ....

....

Triangle C: ....

....

Triangle D: ....

....

Transformations

3 **The grid below shows triangles A and C.**

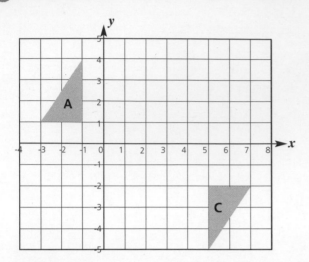

a) Draw the image of triangle A after reflection in the line $x = 2$. Label the image B.

b) Describe fully the transformation that maps triangle B to triangle C.

....

....

4 **The grid below shows shape P.**

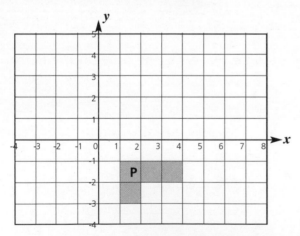

a) Draw the image of shape P after reflection in the line $y = x$. Label the image Q.

b) Draw the image of Q after reflection in the line $x = 1$. Label the image R.

5 **A is a triangle with coordinates (3,1), (5,1) and (5,2).**
   a) On a suitable grid draw triangle A.
   b) i) Reflect triangle A in the line $x = 1$. Label this triangle B.
   ii) Reflect triangle A in the line $y = -1$. Label this triangle C.
   iii) Reflect triangle A in the line $y = x$. Label this triangle D.
   iv) Reflect triangle A in the line $y = -x$. Label this triangle E.

Transformations

1 The grid shows ten shapes A to J.

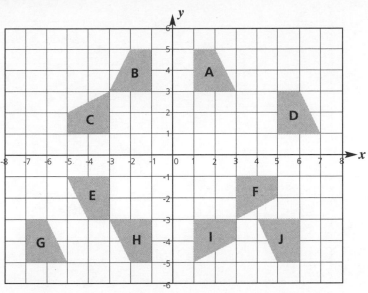

a) Which image is object A rotated…

   i) $\frac{1}{4}$ turn clockwise about the origin (0,0) .... **ii)** $\frac{1}{2}$ turn clockwise about the origin (0,0) ....

   iii) $\frac{3}{4}$ turn clockwise about the origin (0,0) ....

b) Describe the single rotation which takes C to A. ....

2 The grid shows triangle A.

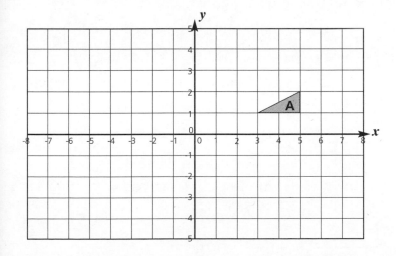

a) Rotate triangle A $\frac{1}{4}$ turn clockwise about the origin (0,0). Label this triangle B.

b) Rotate triangle A $\frac{1}{2}$ turn clockwise about the origin (0,0). Label this triangle C.

c) Rotate triangle A $\frac{3}{4}$ turn clockwise about the origin (0,0). Label this triangle D.

3 A is a quadrilateral with coordinates (2,2), (4,4), (5,3) and (5,1).
   a) On a suitable grid draw quadrilateral A.
   b) i) Rotate quadrilateral A $\frac{1}{4}$ turn clockwise about the origin (0,0). Label this quadrilateral B. **ii)** Rotate quadrilateral A $\frac{1}{2}$ turn clockwise about the origin (0,0). Label this quadrilateral C. **iii)** Rotate quadrilateral A $\frac{3}{4}$ turn clockwise about the origin (0,0). Label this quadrilateral D.

Transformations

1 The grid shows ten triangles A to J.

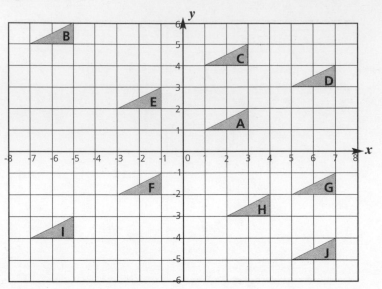

a) Which triangle is object A translated by the vector…

i) $\begin{pmatrix} 4 \\ 2 \end{pmatrix}$ ....

ii) $\begin{pmatrix} 1 \\ -4 \end{pmatrix}$ ....

iii) $\begin{pmatrix} -4 \\ 1 \end{pmatrix}$ ....

iv) $\begin{pmatrix} 0 \\ 3 \end{pmatrix}$ ....

v) $\begin{pmatrix} -8 \\ -5 \end{pmatrix}$ ....

vi) $\begin{pmatrix} 4 \\ -6 \end{pmatrix}$ ....

b) What is the translation vector which maps triangle D onto triangle A? ....

c) What is the translation vector which maps triangle B onto triangle A? ....

2 The grid shows triangle A. Draw and label the following translations.

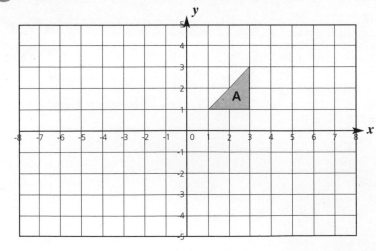

a) Triangle A is mapped onto triangle B by the translation vector $\begin{pmatrix} 4 \\ 2 \end{pmatrix}$

b) Triangle A is mapped onto triangle C by the translation vector $\begin{pmatrix} -5 \\ -4 \end{pmatrix}$

c) Triangle A is mapped onto triangle D by the translation vector $\begin{pmatrix} -8 \\ 0 \end{pmatrix}$

d) Triangle A is mapped onto triangle E by the translation vector $\begin{pmatrix} 5 \\ -6 \end{pmatrix}$

3 A is a triangle with coordinates (-1,-3), (-3,-2) and (-4,-4).
  a) On a suitable grid draw triangle A.
  b) i) Translate triangle A by the vector $\begin{pmatrix} 5 \\ 5 \end{pmatrix}$ Label this triangle B. **ii)** Translate triangle A by the vector $\begin{pmatrix} -5 \\ -5 \end{pmatrix}$ Label this triangle C.

  iii) Translate triangle A by the vector $\begin{pmatrix} 5 \\ -5 \end{pmatrix}$ Label this triangle D. **iv)** Translate triangle A by the vector $\begin{pmatrix} -5 \\ 5 \end{pmatrix}$ Label this triangle E.

Transformations

1 The grid shows triangle A.

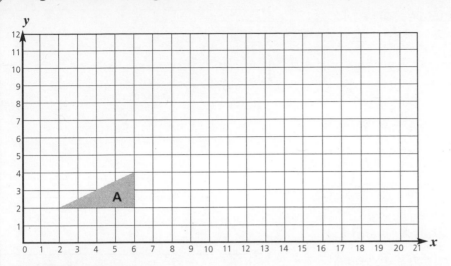

Enlarge triangle A by...

a) a scale factor of 3 about the centre of enlargement (0,0). Label this triangle B.

b) a scale factor of 2 about the centre of enlargement (0,3). Label this triangle C.

c) a scale factor of $\frac{1}{2}$ about the centre of enlargement (0,0). Label this triangle D.

d) a scale factor of 2 about the centre of enlargement (4,0). Label this triangle E.

2 The grid shows three quadrilaterals A, B and C.

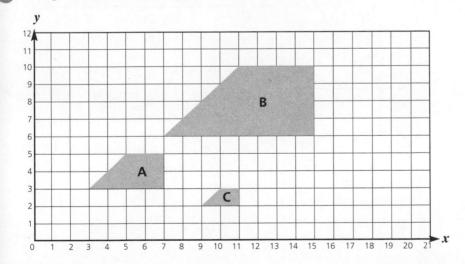

Describe fully the enlargement that would map quadrilateral A...

a) onto B. ....

b) onto C. ....

3 Triangle A has coordinates (3,2), (6,2) and (6,4). **a)** On a suitable grid draw triangle A.
   b) Complete the following enlargements: **i)** Triangle A is enlarged by a scale factor of 2, centre of enlargement (0,0).
   Label this triangle B. **ii)** Triangle A is enlarged by a scale factor of $\frac{1}{2}$, centre of enlargement (0,0). Label this triangle C.
   iii) Triangle A is enlarged by a scale factor of 3, centre of enlargement (1,1). Label this triangle D.

Transformations

1 **The grid shows three triangles A, B and C.**

a) Describe fully a single transformation that would map triangle A onto...

i) triangle B. ....

ii) triangle C. ....

b) Describe fully a single transformation that would map triangle B onto triangle C.

....

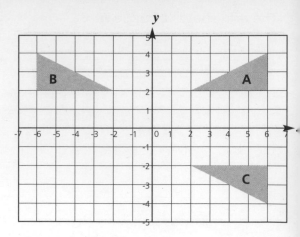

2 **The grid shows three quadrilaterals A, B and C.**

a) Describe fully a single transformation that would map quadrilateral A onto...

i) quadrilateral B ....

ii) quadrilateral C ....

b) Describe fully a single transformation that would map quadrilateral B onto quadrilateral C.

....

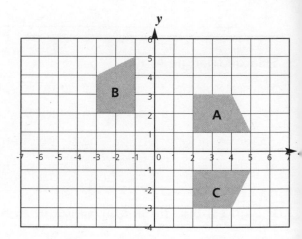

3 **The grid shows triangle A.**

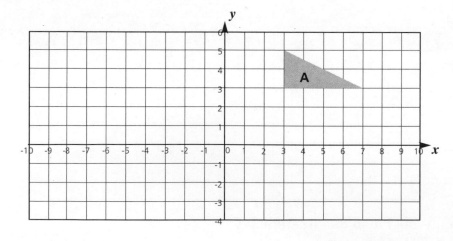

a) Triangle A is reflected in the line $x = 1$. Draw and label this triangle B.

b) Triangle A is reflected in the line $y = 1$. Draw and label this triangle C.

c) Describe fully the single transformation that would map triangle B onto triangle C.

....

....

4 a) Quadrilateral A has coordinates (3,3), (6,3), (7,6) and (5,6). On a suitable grid draw quadrilateral A.

b) Quadrilateral A is reflected in the line $x = 2$. Draw and label quadrilateral B.

c) Quadrilateral A is reflected in the line $y = 0$. Draw and label quadrilateral C.

d) Quadrilateral A is rotated 270° clockwise about the origin (0,0). Draw and label quadrilateral D.

e) Describe fully the single transformation that would map quadrilateral B onto quadrilateral C.

f) Describe fully the single transformation that would map quadrilateral D onto quadrilateral C.

Constructions

For all constructions you must show your construction lines.

1. Construct a triangle ABC with sides AB 4cm, BC 3cm and angle ABC = 40°.

2. On your triangle ABC in question 1 above, construct the bisector of angle BAC.

3. a) Construct a triangle PQR where PQ is 6cm, QR is 5cm and PR is 2cm.

   b) Construct the perpendicular bisector of PQ and where this line meets QR, label it S.

Constructions

4 The sketch opposite shows three towns A, B and C. B is on a bearing of 040° from A. C is due East of A and B is on a bearing of 300° from C. C is 40km from A. Construct an accurate scale drawing.

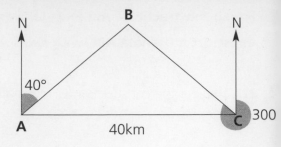

5 Showing all construction lines, and by using a pair of compasses and a ruler, construct the perpendicular bisector of each side of this equilateral triangle.

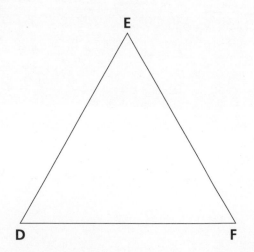

Constructions

6 **Using the line AB below as a starting point, use a pair of compasses and a ruler to...**

a) Construct a 90° angle at A

b) Construct a 90° angle at B

c) Complete the construction to make a square.

A _____ B

7 **In the space below draw a triangle XYZ.**

a) Construct the bisectors of the three angles $\hat{X}$, $\hat{Y}$ and $\hat{Z}$.

b) What do you notice? ....

8 **Using only a ruler and a pair of compasses, construct an equilateral triangle of side 3cm and a square of side 6cm.**

9 **Construct the following triangles using a ruler and a pair of compasses.**

a)

7.4cm 5.3cm

5.3cm

b)

6.2cm

60°

7.3cm

c)

8.4cm

60°

9cm

d)

5.5cm

6.5cm

Loci

1 The points B, C and D represent three schools Biggley, Chiggley and Diggley. Pupils are entitled to a free bus pass if they live within 5km of the school they attend. Some pupils would be entitled to a free bus pass to all three schools. Draw an accurate diagram to show the region in which these pupils live.

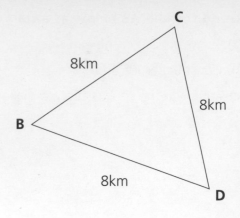

2 A goat is tethered by a rope 4m long to a rail PQ 8m long. The rope can move along the rail from P to Q. Draw an accurate diagram of the locus of points showing the area where the goat can eat grass.

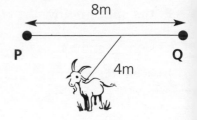

3 Draw a triangle ABC where AB = 7cm, BC = 9cm, $A\hat{B}C$ = 90°.
 a) Draw the locus of points inside the triangle which are equidistant from A and B.
 b) Draw the locus of points inside the triangle which are equidistant from B and C.
 c) Find and label a point D which is equidistant from A and B and equidistant from B and C.

4 Draw the same triangle ABC as for question 3.
 a) Draw the locus of points equidistant from line AB and AC.
 b) A point (P) moves inside triangle ABC, equidistant from AB and AC and greater than 6cm away from C. Show the locus of points where P can move.

3-D Shapes

1 **a)** What shape is the base of the

cuboid shown opposite? ....

b) Which edges are equal in

length to CD? ....

c) Which lengths are equal to AH? ....

d) How many vertices has the cuboid? ....

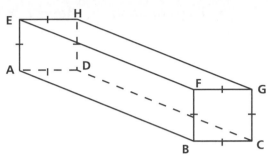

2 **An equilateral triangular prism has a tetrahedron**

placed on top of it. For this combined solid...

a) How many edges does it have? ....

b) How many vertices? ....

c) How many faces? ....

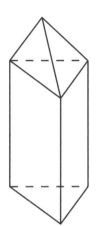

3 **On the grid below draw full size diagrams of the following solids.**

a)

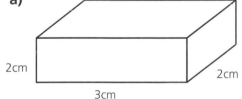

2cm

2cm

3cm

b)

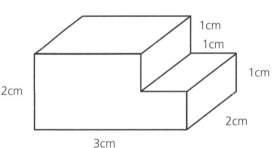

1cm

1cm

1cm

2cm

2cm

3cm

4 **Find the number of faces (_F_), vertices (_V_) and edges (_E_) for this pyramid. Show that _V_ + _F_ − _E_ = 2.**

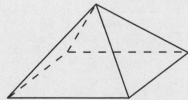

Nets and Elevations

1 **The diagram opposite shows a solid. Draw and label an accurate diagram of the solid showing...**

a) plan view   **b)** front elevation   **c)** side elevation

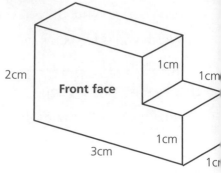

2cm

Front face

1cm

1cm

1cm

3cm

1cm

2 **A net of a solid is shown opposite.**

a) What is the name of the 3-D solid?

....

b) How many vertices does it have?

....

c) Which other corners meet at D? Put an X on each one.

....

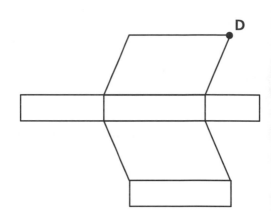

D

3 **Which of the following are nets for a triangular prism? Place a tick beside the correct net(s).**

a)

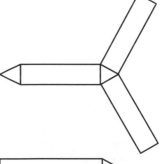

b)

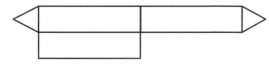

c)

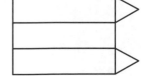

d)

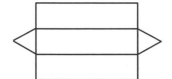

4 **Draw an accurate full-size net of a regular hexagonal prism if each edge is 3cm long.**

5 Draw the **a)** plan **b)** front elevation **c)** side elevation of this solid.

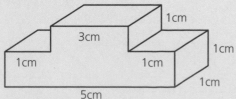

1cm

3cm

1cm

1cm

1cm

1cm

5cm

1 Calculate the volume of the following solids.

a)

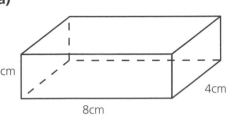

b)

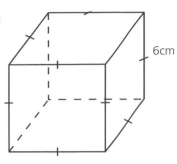

c)

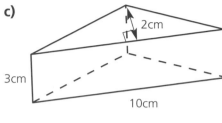

....

....

....

2 Calculate the volume of the following solids.

a)

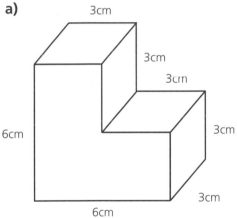

b)

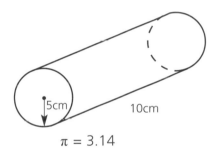

π = 3.14

c)

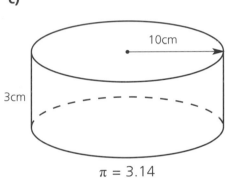

π = 3.14

....

....

....

3 The following solids all have a volume of 100cm³. For each solid, calculate the missing length represented by x.

a)

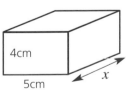

b)

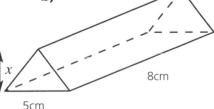

c)

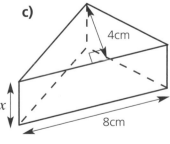

....

....

....

Volume

④ The following cylinders both have a volume of 314cm³. For each cylinder calculate the missing length represented by x (π = 3.14).

a)

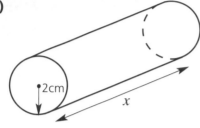

b)

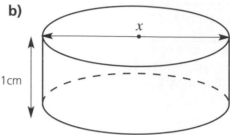

....

....

....

....

....

....

⑤ The tank opposite contains water. The depth of the water is 50cm. All the water is poured into a cylindrical tank which has a diameter of 44cm. Calculate the depth of the water in the cylindrical tank to 1 d.p. (π = 3.14).

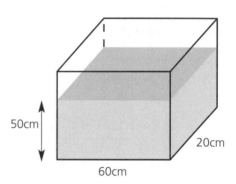

....

....

....

⑥ Calculate the volume of this prism.

Volume = ...

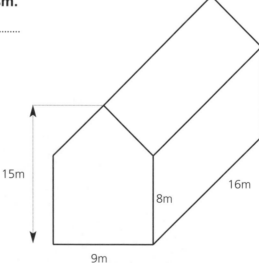

⑦ A cylindrical mug has internal radius 5cm and internal height 8cm.
  a) Calculate the volume of liquid it can hold (to 3 sig. fig.) (π = 3.14).
  b) If 500cm³ of liquid is poured into the mug, what would the depth of liquid be in the mug?

Maps and Scale Drawings

1 **a)** Draw an accurate scale drawing of this garden, using a scale of 1cm to represent 2.5m.

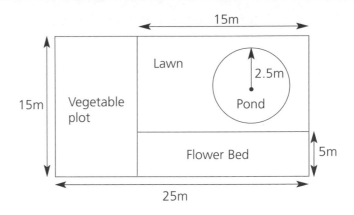

b) By measurement, what is the actual diagonal distance across the garden from corner to corner in metres?

....

2 **This is part of a map of Devon and Cornwall drawn to a scale of 1cm : 10km.**

a) What is the direct distance from Launceston to Exeter?

....

....

b) What is the direct distance between Bodmin and Looe?

....

....

c) Which three places are a direct distance of 43km from Tavistock?

....

....

3 **a)** Draw an accurate scale drawing of a rectangular field 80m long and 50m wide. **b)** By measurement, find the actual distance diagonally from one corner to the opposite corner, to the nearest metre.

4 **The diagram alongside shows a sketch of one side of a house.**
a) Draw an accurate scale drawing using a scale of 1cm to 1m.
b) By measurement, find the actual height of the house (x).

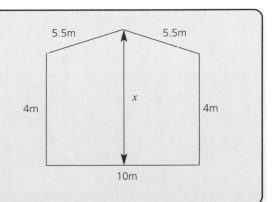

Enlargement, Perimeter, Area & Volume

1 **In the diagram, shape B is an enlargement of shape A with scale factor 2.**

   a) Shape A has perimeter 14cm. What is the perimeter of shape B?

   b) Shape A has area 18cm². What is the area of shape B?

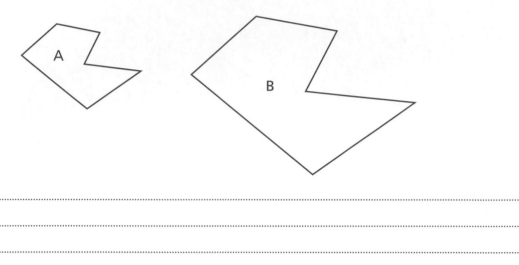

....

....

....

....

2 **Shape A is a triangular prism with volume 20 cm³. Shape B is an enlargement of shape A with scale factor 3. Calculate the volume of shape B.**

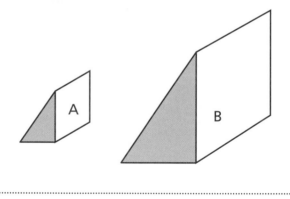

....

....

....

....

3 **A shape with surface area 25cm² and volume 54cm³ is enlarged with scale factor 2.**

   a) What is the surface area of the enlarged shape?

   b) What is the volume of the enlarged shape?

Converting Measurements

1 Convert...

a) 450cm into metres

....

....

b) 3.5 litres into millilitres

....

....

c) 1.25kg into grams

....

....

d) 6874g into kg

....

....

e) 45km into metres

....

....

f) 0.55cm into mm

....

....

2 Convert these lengths into metres.

a) 1005cm

....

....

b) 1.937km

....

....

c) 2650mm

....

....

3 Put these weights into order of size, smallest first.

420g   4kg   39.5kg   4220mg   0.405kg

....

....

....

4 Convert...

a) 45cm into inches

....

....

b) 6 ounces into grams

....

....

c) 5 gallons into litres

....

....

5 Terry is 1.5m tall. Jake is 68 inches tall. Who is the tallest and by how much?

....

....

....

6 Put these lengths into decreasing order of size:

1km   900m   1200m   11 000cm   1 050 000mm

7 Convert...

a) 3 miles into km **b)** 12km into miles **c)** 4.5 pounds into grams **d)** 360g into pounds **e)** 12 pints into litres

f) 22.5 litres into pints

8 Sue ran a 10km race. How many yards did she run altogether? (1760 yards = 1 mile).

Bearings

1 The diagram shows the position of the coastguard (C), the beach (B) and a yacht (Y).

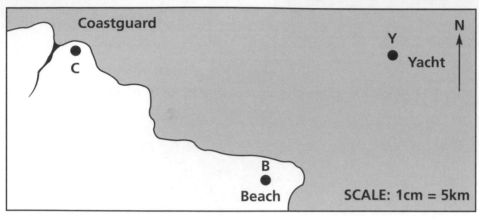

a) What is the bearing of…

    i) Y from C? .... **ii)** Y from B? ....

    iii) B from C? .... **iv)** B from Y? ....

    v) C from Y? .... **vi)** C from B? ....

b) What is the actual distance from…

    i) C to B? .... **ii)** C to Y? .... **iii)** B to Y? ....

2 The map shows the position of 4 towns A, B, C and D on an island. A helicopter flies directly from A to B, then B to C, then C to D and finally D back to A. On what four bearings must it fly?

A ➤ B ....

B ➤ C ....

C ➤ D ....

D ➤ A ....

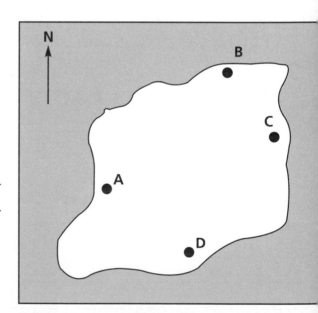

3 An explorer walks 1000m on a bearing of 070° and then walks 2000m on a bearing of 160°.
    a) Draw an accurate scale drawing of his route.
    b) By measurement, find the bearing he must follow to return directly to his starting point.

4 Treasure is buried on an island according to the following instructions: "The treasure lies on a bearing of 100° from the coconut tree and on a bearing of 200° from the cactus plant. The cactus plant is 20m due east of the coconut tree." Draw a scale drawing using 1cm to 5m to show the position of the treasure.

Compound Measures

1 Work out the time taken to travel 92km at an average speed of 55km/h.

....89

....

....

....

2 A marathon runner completes 26.2 miles in a course record of 2hrs 20mins.
What was his average speed?

....

....

....

....

3 A tortoise takes 20 minutes to get from one end of the garden to the other. His average speed
was 2cm per second. How long is the garden in metres?

....

....

....

....

4 A boat travels for $2\frac{1}{2}$ hours at 100km/h and then $1\frac{1}{2}$ hours at 80km/h. Calculate its average speed
for the whole journey.

....

....

....

....

5 **a)** Change 30 metres per second into km per hour.
b) A car travels 30 metres per second for $3\frac{1}{2}$ hours. How far does it travel in km?

Measuring Lines and Angles

1 Measure the length of AB to the nearest 0.1 cm.

A ——————————————————————————————— B

....

2 Measure the length of the diagonal PR of this rectangle in cm to 1 decimal place.

....

3 Measure the size of angles *x* and *y* to the nearest degree.

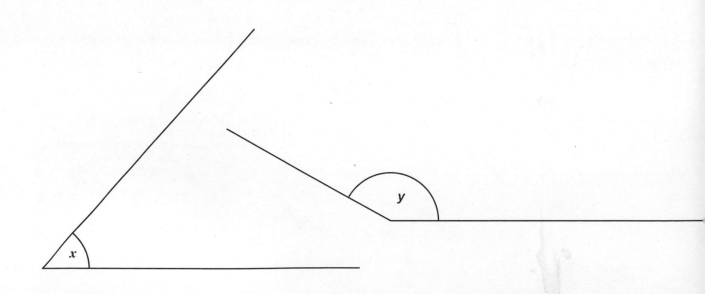

....

4 Draw a line AB of length 7cm. Draw a line BC of length 10cm such that angle ABC = 80°. Measure the length of AC.

Probability

1 **Tim has ten cards (shown below). They are placed face down and mixed up.**

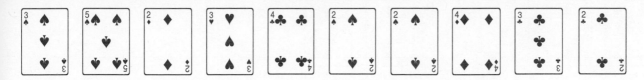

a) What is the probability that a card picked at random will be…

i) a 2? .... **ii)** a 3? .... **iii)** a 4? ....

iv) a 5? .... **v)** not a 2? .... **vi)** not a 3? ....

b) Here is a probability scale:

```
                              0.5
0 |----+----+----+----+----+----+----+----+----+----| 1
```

On the scale above…

i) mark with an A the probability that a card picked at random will be a 2.

ii) mark with a B the probability that a card picked at random will be a 3.

iii) mark with a C the probability that a card picked at random will be a 4.

iv) mark with a D the probability that a card picked at random will be a 5.

2 **A bag contains 4 red counters, 5 blue counters and 9 yellow counters.**

A counter is selected at random. What is the probability that it is…

a) red? .... **b)** not red? .... **c)** blue? ....

d) not blue? .... **e)** yellow? .... **f)** not yellow? ....

3 **A page in a calendar shows the month of June.**

If a date is chosen at random, what is the probability that it is…

a) an even number? .... **b)** an odd number? ....

c) a prime number? .... **d)** a weekday? ....

e) not a weekday? ....

4 **Jack has the following fair spinner. He spins it.**

a) What is the probability that the spinner does not land on a 1?

....

b) What is the probability that the spinner does not land on a 2?

....

c) What is the probability that the spinner lands on a 3?

....

Probability

5 Vicky has two sets of cards, A and B as shown below:

a) Complete all the possible outcomes if two cards are picked, one from A and one from B, at random.

b) What is the probability that the two cards picked are **i)** both 2s? ....

   ii) both the same suit? .... **iii)** not the same suit? ....

6 Brian's pencil case contains blue, black, red and green pens only. The probability of picking out a pen of a certain colour is shown in the table. What is the probability that the pen picked out is red?

Colour of pen	Probability of picking that colour
Blue	0.2
Black	0.35
Red	....
Green	0.15

7 On her way to work, Safia has to drive through heavy traffic. The probability that Safia will arrive at work on time is 0.4 and that she will arrive late is 0.25. What is the probability that she will arrive early?

....

8 A bag contains 8 blue marbles, 6 red marbles and 2 green marbles. One marble is pulled out at random.

a) What is the probability that the marble picked out is green?

....

b) What is the probability that the marble picked out is blue?

....

9 A box contains 7 red balls and 3 blue balls. A ball is picked out at random.
What is the probability that it is **a)** red? **b)** not red? **c)** blue? **d)** not blue? **e)** red or blue? **f)** black?

10 A kitchen cupboard contains tins of baked beans, peas, carrots and potatoes only. The probability of picking a tin of potatoes is $\frac{1}{12}$, while the probability of picking a tin of carrots is three times that of a tin of potatoes, and a tin of peas is twice that of a tin of carrots.
   a) What is the probability of picking **i)** a tin of carrots? **ii)** a tin of peas? **iii)** a tin of baked beans?
   b) What is the probability of not picking **i)** a tin of carrots? **ii)** a tin of peas? **iii)** a tin of baked beans?
   c) If the cupboard contains 4 tins of baked beans, how many tins are there in the cupboard altogether?

Probability

1 **Two fair dice are thrown. The two numbers are added together to give a total score.**

a) Complete the sample space diagram below to show all the scores:

		First Die				
	1	**2**	**3**	**4**	**5**	**6**
1	2	3	4			
2	3	4				
3	4					
4						
5						
6						

Second Die (left axis label)

b) What is the probability that the total score will be...

i) equal to 7? ....

ii) greater than 7? ....

iii) a prime number? ....

iv) a square number? ....

v) greater than 12? ....

vi) a multiple of 3? ....

vii) a factor of 12? ....

2 **Francis has the following coins in her pocket:**   **Jim has the following coins in his pocket:**

Two coins are picked out at random, one from Francis's pocket and one from Jim's pocket.

The values of the two coins are added together.

a) Complete the sample space diagram below to show all the values:

	Francis's Coin					

Jim's Coin (left axis label)

b) What is the probability that the total value of the two coins added together is...

i) equal to 6p? ....

ii) equal to 11p? ....

iii) less than 10p? ....

iv) greater than 40p? ....

v) less than 40p? ....

vi) equal to 40p? ....

---

3 **Bruce has an ordinary fair die. Robin has the following fair spinner:**

The spinner is spun and the die is thrown to give two numbers.

a) Draw a sample space diagram to show all the possible scores if the numbers are multiplied together.

b) What is the probability that the score is **i)** equal to 12? **ii)** equal to 24? **iii)** a multiple of 10?

iv) a factor of 4? **v)** an odd number? **vi)** an even number?

Probability

1 **The following fair spinner is spun 120 times:**

a) How many times would you expect the spinner to land on…

   i) a 1? .... **ii)** a 2? .... **iii)** a 3? ....

b) The actual number of times the spinner landed on a 1, 2 and 3 is shown in the table below. For each number calculate the estimated probability.

Number	Number of times landed	Estimated probability
1	66	....
2	38	....
3	16	....

2 **Jane tosses a coin 50, 100, 150, 200 and 250 times. She records the number of tails she gets in a table (opposite):**

a) Complete the table by calculating the missing estimated probability.

b) On the grid below draw a bar graph to show the estimated probability of the coin landing on tails.

c) If Jane kept tossing the coin, what would you expect the estimated probability of the coin landing on tails to become? Explain why.

....
....
....
....
....
....

Number of tosses	Number of tails	Estimated probability
50	20	0.4
100	44	....
150	80	....
200	92	....
250	120	....

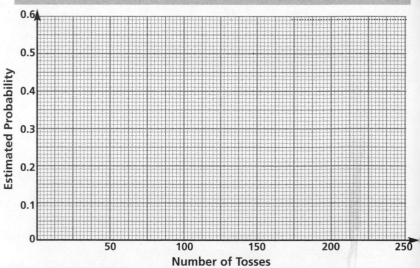

3 **Below are the results of an experiment where a fair die was thrown and the number of 6s were recorded.**

Number of throws	30	60	90	120	150	180	210	240	270	300	330	360
Number of 6s thrown	3	5	10	16	23	28	35	42	47	49	52	59
Estimated probability												

a) Complete the table by calculating the missing estimated probability (to 2 d.p.).

b) Draw a bar graph to show the estimated probability of throwing a 6.

c) How many 6s would you expect to be thrown if the experiment was continued and the die was thrown 1500 times?

Problem Solving and Data Handling

1 Fill in the empty boxes in this flow chart to complete the data handling cycle.

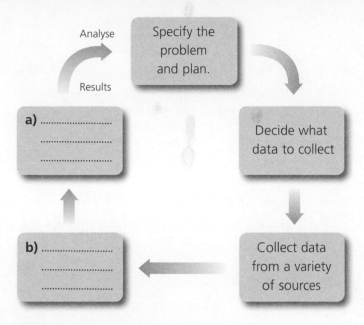

Analyse

Specify the problem and plan.

Results

a) ....
....
....

Decide what data to collect

b) ....
....
....

Collect data from a variety of sources

2 Give three examples of possible sources of data.

a) ....

b) ....

c) ....

3 You are asked to conduct research into the amount of exercise that your classmates take outside of school. Using the data handling cycle explain what processes you will go through in order to observe, collect and make a conclusion from your research. Suggest some possible ways in which the research might be developed further.

....

....

....

....

....

....

4 Suggest another problem for which you could use the data handling cycle.

....

....

....

Collecting Data

1 **What is the difference between primary data and secondary data?**

....

....

....

2 **a)** What is sampling?

....

....

b) A recent survey carried out in Manchester suggests that 90% of the national population prefer football to rugby. The survey was conducted on 200 males. Has this survey provided reliable data? Explain why.

....

....

....

....

3 **Jenny is concerned about the breakfast habits of the pupils in her school. She decides to use a questionnaire to find out what pupils have to eat for breakfast. She has chosen eight questions for her questionnaire. Decide whether each question is suitable or not suitable, giving a reason for your answer.**

a) Everybody should eat breakfast. Don't you agree?

....

b) Do you eat breakfast?

....

c) What time do you get up in the morning?

....

d) Are you a vegetarian?

....

e) What year are you?

....

f) What do you have to eat if you have breakfast?

....

g) If you eat breakfast do you have cereal, toast or other?

....

h) Do you brush your teeth before breakfast?

....

Collecting Data

4 Joe works in a supermarket. He decides to use a questionnaire to find out about the shopping habits of the customers who come into the store. Here is the first question:

'How old are you?' Tick the correct box.

Under 10 years		11 years to 20 years		21 years to 40 years		41 years to 60 years		61 years to 80 years		Over 80 years	

a) Make up two more suitable questions Joe could use for his questionnaire.

....

....

b) Make up two questions which would not be suitable for his questionnaire.

....

....

5 In a survey a group of pupils were asked, 'How long did you spend watching TV over the weekend?'

a) Design a suitable data capture sheet to collect this information.

b) How would you make sure that the information obtained was from a random sample?

....

....

6 Molly works in a pizza parlour. She decides to use a questionnaire to find out about the eating habits of the people who come into the parlour.
  a) Make up three suitable questions Molly could use for her questionnaire.
  b) Make up three questions which are not suitable for her questionnaire.

7 Jimmy is carrying out a survey to investigate what the pupils in his school spend their pocket money on.
  a) Design a suitable observation sheet for him to collect the information.
  b) How could Jimmy make sure that the information collected was random.

Sorting Data

1. **What is the difference between discrete and continuous data?**

....

....

....

....

2. **Jane is carrying out a traffic survey. She records the number of cars that pass her house every 30 seconds for a period of 20 minutes. Group her data by completing the frequency table below.**

Number of cars

4 3 4 ~~1~~ 2 5 5 4 3 2

4 5 3 2 4 4 4 5 5 ~~1~~

2 4 3 5 4 3 3 5 2 4

2 4 3 5 2 ~~1~~ ~~1~~ 4 5 3

Number of Cars	Tally	Frequency
1	IIII	4
2		
3		
4		
5		

3. **A survey was carried out on the number of residents in each house on a street.**

   The results are given below:

   4 5 3 4 3 6 1 5 4 2 3 4 5 2 4 5 5 3 4 6

   4 2 5 3 5 2 4 3 4 1 3 4 4 1 5 2 4 5 3 4

   a) In the space below group together the results in a frequency table.

   b) What percentage of the houses have 3 or more residents? ....

Sorting Data

4 The test results for a group of students are given below.

Group the data to complete the frequency table below.

31	61	40	63	65
78	52	57	~~15~~	35
77	~~21~~	68	46	68
64	70	26	87	49

Test Mark	Tally	Frequency
0–19	II	2
20–39		
40–59		
60–79		
80–99		

5 John has recorded the temperature at midday every day for the month of June using a thermometer. All the temperatures are to the nearest degree Celsius.

a) Group together John's results by completing the frequency table.

Temperature (°C)	Tally	Frequency
$5 \leqslant T < 10$		
$10 \leqslant T < 15$		
$15 \leqslant T < 20$		
$20 \leqslant T < 25$		

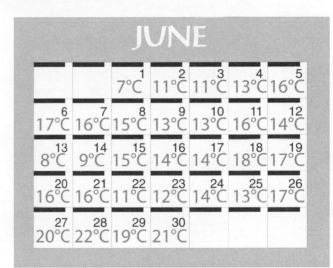

JUNE

		1	2	3	4	5
		7°C	11°C	11°C	13°C	16°C
6	7	8	9	10	11	12
17°C	16°C	15°C	13°C	13°C	16°C	14°C
13	14	15	16	17	18	19
8°C	9°C	15°C	14°C	14°C	18°C	17°C
20	21	22	23	24	25	26
16°C	16°C	11°C	12°C	14°C	13°C	17°C
27	28	29	30			
20°C	22°C	19°C	21°C			

b) What percentage of the recorded midday temperatures in June are 15°C or more?

....

6 Bolton Wanderers scored the following number of goals in Premier League matches for the 2002/2003 season.
1 1 1 1 2 1 1 0 1 1 1 1 1 4 1 0 1 0 1 4
0 0 0 1 0 1 4 1 1 0 2 1 2 0 1 0 2 0 2
Group together the data in a frequency table.

7 Emma decided to measure the height (h) of all the students in her class.
Here are the results, to the nearest cm:
171 178 166 173 180 173 186 176 170 184 178 174 169 189 175
182 181 171 179 164 178 175 174 191 169 178 173 188 167 192
a) Sort the data into a frequency table using class intervals $160 \leqslant h < 165$, $165 \leqslant h < 170$ etc.
b) What percentage of the students in Emma's class have a height measurement of 170cm or more?

8 The individual weights of 40 people, to the nearest kg, are as follows:
79 75 68 70 83 72 81 89 61 74 80 51 84 63 73 54 76 74 80 85
94 77 71 81 70 66 87 62 59 63 63 67 75 81 80 78 60 77 61 75
Sort the data into a frequency table using appropriate class intervals.

Sorting Data

1 The following data shows the age (in years) of 30 shoppers in a supermarket.

41 51 8 60 21 31 41 17 68 28 34 45 46 52 74
56 10 23 47 30 34 9 42 29 55 44 38 57 47 58

Using tens to form the 'stem' and units to form the 'leaves', draw a stem and leaf diagram to show the data.

2 A survey of 120 people was conducted to find out if they listened to the radio whilst driving. Complete the two way table to show the results.

	Men	Women	Total
Listen to Radio	32		73
Do Not Listen to Radio		24	
Total	55		

3 A survey of 200 Year 7, 8 and 9 pupils was carried out to find their favourite type of music from a choice of three: Pop, Rap or Dance.

a) Complete the two way table to show the results.

	Year 7	Year 8	Year 9	Total
Pop	42		18	
Rap		12		41
Dance	14		31	69
Total			62	

b) What percentage of the pupils chose Pop as their favourite type of music?

....

4 Here are the heights, to the nearest cm, of 30 students in a class:
171 178 166 173 180 173 186 176 170 184 178 174 169 189 175
182 181 171 179 164 178 175 174 191 169 178 173 188 167 192.
a) Using tens to form the 'stem' and units to form the 'leaves' draw a stem and leaf digram to show the data.
b) What is the modal class of the data?
c) What is the median value of the data?

Displaying Data

1. A survey was carried out to find the favourite type of music for a group of people. The results are displayed in this pictogram.

   Country
   Pop
   Classical
   Jazz
   Rock

   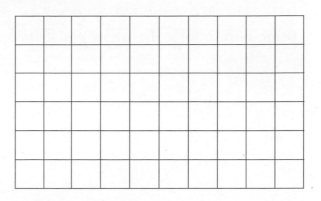

   Where ⬤ represents four people.

   Draw a bar graph to show this information.

2. 36 primary school children were asked to name their favourite pet.

   $\frac{1}{3}$ said DOG

   $\frac{1}{4}$ said CAT

   $\frac{2}{9}$ said FISH

   $\frac{1}{12}$ said RABBIT

   The remainder said BIRD.

   Draw a bar graph to show this information.

3. This composite bar chart shows how the amounts of full fat milk and semi-skimmed milk sold by a supermarket each day changed from the year 2000 to the year 2010.

   a) In which year was the total amount of milk sold the greatest?

   ....

   b) Describe the main change between 2000 and 2010.

   ....

   ....

   c) Give a possible reason for your answer to part b).

   ....

   ....

   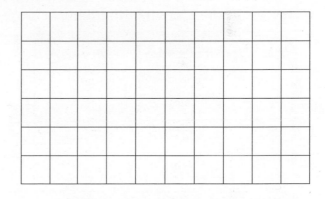

   Key
   ☐ Semi-skimmed
   ▦ Full fat

Displaying Data

1 The table shows the height of a girl from birth to age 5. Her height was recorded every year on her birthday.

Height (cm)	42	51	66	75	84	89
Time (years)	0	1	2	3	4	5

Plot the information given in the table as points on the graph.
Join the points with straight lines to show how her height charged.

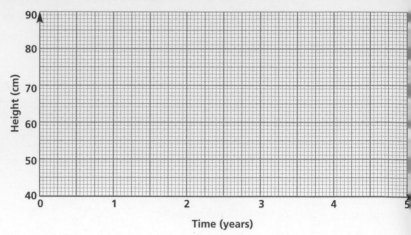

2 In a survey 50 women were asked how much they spend on cosmetics in one week. The results are shown in the table below.

Money Spent, M (£)	Frequency
$0 \leqslant M < 2$	1
$2 \leqslant M < 4$	6
$4 \leqslant M < 6$	28
$6 \leqslant M < 8$	11
$8 \leqslant M < 10$	4

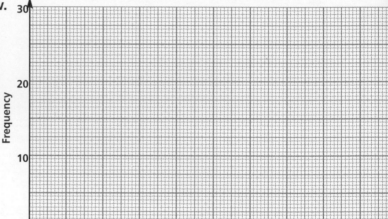

a) Draw a frequency polygon on the graph paper opposite to show the information.

b) 50 men were also asked how much they spend on toiletries in one week. The results are shown opposite. On the same axes draw a frequency polygon to show the money spent by men.

c) How do the two distributions compare?

....

....

....

....

Money Spent, M (£)	Frequency
$0 \leqslant M < 2$	13
$2 \leqslant M < 4$	28
$4 \leqslant M < 6$	5
$6 \leqslant M < 8$	3
$8 \leqslant M < 10$	1

3 Below are the highest recorded temperatures, in °C, on one particular day for forty places around the world.

17   28   33   19   21   28   31   24   21   20   19   28   24   19   20   24   29   32   16   26
33   24   23   16   16   20   28   17   24   23   26   31   33   18   31   26   28   19   19   21

a) Group together the data in a frequency table.
b) Construct a frequency diagram to show the data.
c) On separate axes construct a frequency polygon to show the data.

Displaying Data

1. **This scatter diagram shows the average journey time and distance travelled for ten pupils travelling from home to school.**

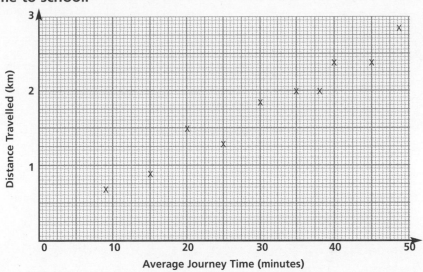

a) What does the scatter diagram tell you about the relationship between the journey time and the distance travelled?

....

b) Draw a line of best fit.

c) Use your graph to estimate...

   i) the time taken by John, who travelled a distance of 2.5 km. ....

   ii) the distance travelled by Donna, who takes 27 minutes. ....

2. **The table below shows the heights and weights of 10 boys.**

Height (cm)	133	162	130	163	153
Weight (kg)	70	84	64	87	87

Height (cm)	150	124	141	150	138
Weight (kg)	77	66	79	82	69

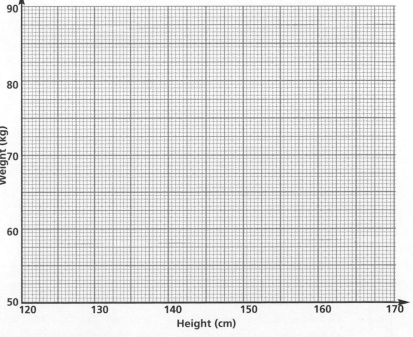

a) Use the information given to plot a scatter diagram, including line of best fit.

b) What type of correlation is there between height and weight?

....

c) **i)** Tony weighs 72kg. Use your graph to estimate his height. ....

   ii) Rob is 1.57m tall. Use your graph to estimate his weight. ....

3 Mrs Thrift goes shopping at her local supermarket on 12 separate occasions. Each time she pays for her items with a £10 note. The table below shows the number of items bought and change received.

Change received (£)	2.50	5.60	5.70	7.80	0.90	3.10	5.20	4.20	1.50	7.90	6.80	2.70
Number of items bought	10	8	6	4	14	12	7	8	14	2	7	11

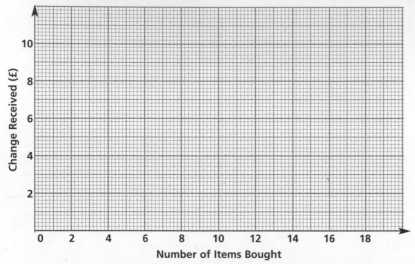

a) Use the information given to plot a scatter diagram including line of best fit.

b) What type of correlation does the scatter diagram show? ....
....

c) i) Mrs Thrift buys 9 items. Estimate how much change she receives. ....

   ii) Mrs Thrift receives £6.20 in change. Estimate how many items she bought.
....

4 The table below shows the number of tracks and total playing time for 12 music CDs.

Number of tracks	14	20	8	11	18	14
Total time (mins)	62	69	58	61	66	67

Number of tracks	10	5	16	7	18	6
Total time (mins)	56	46	66	56	69	52

a) Use the information given to plot a scatter diagram including line of best fit.

b) i) If a CD has 13 tracks, estimate its total playing time. ....

   ii) If the total playing time of a CD is 54 minutes, estimate the number of tracks it has. ....

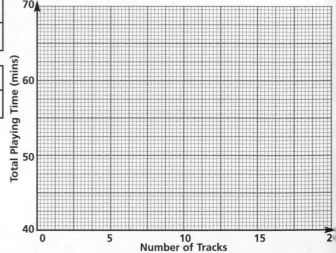

5 The table gives information about the number of chapters and the total number of pages in books on Diane's shelf.

Number of chapters	19	28	11	14	27	23	8	16	21	25	32	19	35	11	16
Total number of pages	250	355	110	230	235	350	145	200	235	315	325	120	395	125	305

a) Use the information given to plot a scatter diagram including line of best fit.

b) What does the scatter diagram tell you about the relationship between the number of chapters and total number of pages?

c) Use your graph to estimate **i)** the total pages if a book has 24 chapters

   ii) the number of chapters if a book has 190 pages.

Displaying Data

1 In one week a travel agent sold 120 separate holidays. The table below shows the holiday destinations.

Holiday Destination	No. of holidays sold
Spain	42
Greece	12
France	34
Cyprus	22
Italy	10

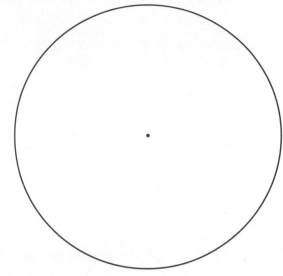

a) Draw and label a pie chart to represent these destinations.

b) What percentage of the holidays sold were for Spain?

....

c) What fraction of the holidays sold were for Greece? ....

2 60 men and 60 women were asked, 'What is your favourite colour of car?'
The two pie charts show the results.

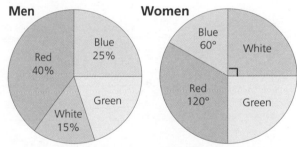

a) i) How many men chose red as their favourite colour?

....

ii) How many women chose red as their favourite colour?

....

b) Did more men or women choose green as their favourite colour? Show your working. ....

....

3 This table shows the number of telephone calls Mrs Chattergee makes in one week.

Day of the week	Monday	Tuesday	Wednesday	Thursday	Friday	Saturday	Sunday
Number of phone calls	3	2	8	4	7	10	6

a) Draw and label a pie chart to represent the information.
b) What percentage of the telephone calls were made at the weekend?

4 The ages of the people living in Addick Close are as follows:
2 24 14 8 70 15 19 31 85 4 3 12 30 27 45 50 66 68 2 11
74 31 63 28 41 47 51 14 18 83 69 7 52 35 33 20 14 6 7 5.
a) Construct a frequency table to show the distribution of ages using class intervals of 1–20, 21–40, etc.
b) Draw and label a pie chart to show the distribution. **c)** What percentage of the residents are aged 41 or over?

5 A group of men and women were asked how they travel to work.
The two pie charts show their responses. They are not drawn accurately.

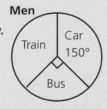
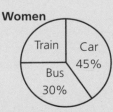

a) If 10 men travel to work by car, how many men travel to work by **i)** bus? **ii)** train?
b) If 20 women travel to work by train, how many women travel to work by **i)** car? **ii)** bus?

Averages and Spread

1 Laura has the following coins in her pocket:

Calculate the mean, median, mode and range for the value of the coins.

Mean: ....

Median: .... Mode: .... Range: ....

2 The table below shows the results of an Internet search for the price of a particular camera.

Calculate the mean, mode, median and range of the camera prices.

Camera	Cost (£)	Camera	Cost (£)	Camera	Cost (£)	Camera	Cost (£)	Camera	Cost (£)
1	227	5	169	9	225	13	211	17	155
2	246	6	204	10	210	14	248	18	153
3	248	7	220	11	239	15	166	19	196
4	248	8	165	12	227	16	170	20	173

Mean: ....

Median: .... Mode: .... Range: ....

3 The weights of the 11 players in the Year 11 hockey team were measured.

Their weights in kilograms were: 51 60 62 47 53 48 52 51 65 61 66

a) Calculate the mean, median, mode and range for their weights.

Mean: ....

Median: .... Mode: .... Range: ....

b) The weights of the 11 players in the Year 10 hockey team were also measured.

Their mean was 52.5kg and the range was 11kg. Compare the weights of the two teams.

....

....

4 9A contains 14 girls. Their heights in metres are:

1.46   1.62   1.57   1.6   1.39   1.71   1.53   1.62   1.58   1.40   1.46   1.63   1.62   1.65

a) Calculate the mean, median, mode and range for the heights.

b) The boys in 9A have a mean height of 1.68m and a range of 0.32m. Compare the heights of the girls and the boys.

Averages and Spread

1 Janet carries out a survey on the number of passengers in cars which pass her house.
Here are the results:

Number of passengers	Frequency	Frequency × No. of passengers
0	11	
1	12	
2	6	
3	8	
4	3	

a) How many cars were there in her survey? ....

b) What is the modal number of passengers? ....

c) What is the median number of passengers? ....

d) What is the range of the number of passengers? ....

e) What is the mean number of passengers?

....

....

2 This graph shows the number of chocolate bars bought by pupils at a school tuck shop.

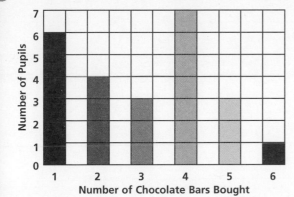

a) How many pupils bought chocolate bars? ....

b) What is the modal number of bars bought? ....

c) What is the median number of bars bought? ....

d) What is the mean number of bars bought?

....

....

....

3 Phil carries out a survey about the amount of pocket money his classmates each receive every week. The results are shown below.

Amount of pocket money, M (£)	Frequency		
$0 \leqslant M < 2$	3		
$2 \leqslant M < 4$	15		
$4 \leqslant M < 6$	8		
$6 \leqslant M < 8$	5		
$8 \leqslant M < 10$	1		

a) Calculate an estimate of the mean amount of pocket money the pupils receive. ....

b) In which class interval does the median lie? ....

c) What is the modal class? ....

4 During a PE lesson the boys have a 100m race. Their times were recorded and the results are shown below:

Time taken, t (seconds)	$12 < t \leqslant 14$	$14 < t \leqslant 16$	$16 < t \leqslant 18$	$18 < t \leqslant 20$	$20 < t \leqslant 22$	$22 < t \leqslant 24$
Number of boys	2	9	13	5	3	1

a) Calculate an estimate of the mean time **b)** In which class interval does the median lie? **c)** Which is the modal class?

Unstructured Exam-style Questions

1. **Josh plans to visit a friend by car.**

   The total distance is 60 miles.

   $\frac{2}{5}$ **of this distance would be at an average speed of 30 mph.**

   The remaining distance would be at an average speed of 40 mph.

   Josh needs to arrive no later than 3 pm. What is the latest time that he can leave?

Unstructured Exam-style Questions

2 **A car hire company offers two deals to its customers.**

Deal 1	Deal 2
Daily charge £25 plus 10p per mile.	Daily charge £55 First 400 miles free then add 20p per mile.

Compare the costs for 1 day's car hire using the two deals and show which is better if the mileage is:

a) 100 miles

....

....

....

....

....

....

b) 350 miles

....

....

....

....

....

....

c) 600 miles.

....

....

....

....

....

....

Unstructured Exam-style Questions

3 **A taxi firm has 3 types of vehicle available that carry different numbers of passengers.**

Capacity/passengers	Up to 4	Up to 6	Up to 10
Cost	£4.50 + £1 per mile	£6.50 + £1.50 per mile	£8 + £2 per mile

Calculate the minimum cost to transport a group of people 6 miles if the number of people in the group is:

a) 3

....

....

....

....

....

b) 6

....

....

....

....

....

c) 9

....

....

....

....

....

Unstructured Exam-style Questions

4) A house valued at £250 000 increases in value by 12% in one year, then by a further 11% in the second year but then falls in value by 15% in the third year.

What is the value of the house at the end of the third year?

Notes